THE COST ANALYST'S

COMPANION

THE COST ANALYST'S COMPANION

David A. Lee

Logistics Management Institute

McLean, Virginia USA

ISBN 0-9661916-0-9

Library of Congress Catalog Card Number: 97-76098

2nd printing, 2003

Printed in the United States of America.

This book is printed on acid-free, recycled paper.

To Milt
with respect
and affection

CONTENTS

FOREWORD

The table of contents of this book lists what for the experienced cost estimator is a familiar set of topics. This does not mean, however, that the book is directed at beginners. The opposite is more nearly true, and the book can be read profitably by all cost analysts who think carefully about their craft.

David Lee brought to the writing of this book both a high level of intellectual rigor, gained as an applied mathematician and a faculty member at the Air Force Institute of Technology, and seven years of experience supervising the development of cost estimates by the Cost Analysis Improvement Group (CAIG) of the Office of the Secretary of Defense. He was intimately involved in the preparation of cost estimates for more than 50 major weapon systems, including such contentious estimates as those for the F-22 at Milestone II, the Strategic Defense Initiative Strategic Defense System, and Javelin, among many others. I point to the depth and breadth of David Lee's experience with cost estimation to insist that, while his tone is often "theoretical" (or, better, highly analytical), he writes from a practical perspective.

There is no important inconsistency in this for those of us who share David Lee's belief that complex, ambiguous situations and availability of only incomplete and somewhat suspect data are no excuse for sloppy thinking or careless statistics. To the contrary, as David Lee points out, getting useful results in these situations requires great care, especially care and ingenuity in applying quantitative techniques.

I strongly agree with David Lee on this matter and regard it as central to high quality cost estimation. Accordingly, both as an exercise in that mode of thought and for the results, I recommend this book to those who, whatever their level of experience, wish to become better cost analysts.

David McNicol

Chairman,
Cost Analysis Improvement Group

Acknowledgments

I am particularly grateful to Walt Cooper, who had the idea that the notes for a series of lectures that I gave to the staff of the Cost Analysis Improvement Group in the Office of the Secretary of Defense staff could be made into a book, and to John Dukovich, who managed the book's production, made effective figures out of my crude ones, and whose perceptive questions eliminated a great deal of unclear writing.

It's a pleasure to acknowledge the invaluable help of those who made detailed comments on my draft: economists Gary Bliss and Dennis Smallwood, cost analyst James Herd, and statistician Richard Kulp. They are responsible for many of the book's strong points; responsibility for any weak ones is mine.

I owe a great debt to David McNicol, Chairman of the OSD CAIG, who sponsored the lectures from which the book developed. I deeply appreciate his wise comments on the text and kind encouragement during the writing.

It would be difficult to thank adequately all involved colleagues at the Logistics Management Institute, particularly Don Srull, John Wallace, and Robert Hemm, for many helpful discussions. Fortunately, everyone can see the results of the expert professional work of Suzan Glosser, Kathy Myers, Karen Moyes, and Daniel Hirschhorn in book design and editing.

The book owes its existence to the willingness of the Logistics Management Institute, particularly its president, General William G. T. Tuttle, Jr., to publish the work. I thank them heartily.

David A. Lee

INTRODUCTION

This book is intended to be a convenient source of ideas and methods (a companion) for practicing cost analysts. It deals with five areas:

- A global perspective of cost analysis and estimating as applications of system identification

- The nature and use of cost-progress curves

- The use and development of cost-estimating relations

- The application of Rayleigh methods for analyzing development program costs

- The implementation of engineering and statistical principles when estimating operating and support costs.

Some of the material, like the introduction to cost-estimating relations, is elementary. These parts probably will be useful mostly to people who have limited experience in cost analysis. Other parts, like the discussion of system identification as a paradigm for cost analysis and the section on using physical principles to make cost-estimating relationships, are intended to be interesting and useful to the experienced practitioner.

The approach in each of the five areas of consideration is to base cost analyses on principles of economics, physics, and technology, and to develop them with careful applications of mathematics and statistics. Working this way may seem unnecessarily fussy. The complex situations cost analysts must treat usually far exceed what can be modeled completely from first principles. Almost always, cost estimates and analyses need inputs from experience, known as "analysts' judgments." Since judgment will always play an essential role, why bother with careful modeling and analysis?

Precisely because judgment is essential, it is vitally important for cost analysts to get as much help as possible from rational applications of physics, economics, technology, mathematics, and statistics. In this way, the number of analysts' judgment calls is kept small. Each one is clearly identified, and the effects of its uncertainties can be assessed.

Fuzzy economics and physics and the sloppy use of mathematical and statistical tools introduce uncertainties (or downright errors) into estimates. These gratuitous uncertainties are hard to track. They tend to amplify uncertainties introduced by truly necessary judgment inputs, and they make it hard to tell when judgment really is required.

Estimates and analyses made with careful attention to underlying principles, and to mathematical and statistical developments, are much easier to communicate and are more likely to be accurate than those made less carefully. When practices like "Cost as an Independent Variable" in the United States' defense acquisition community make cost estimates an integral part of system design, the careful approach really does seem to be the only way to go.

CHAPTER 1

SYSTEM IDENTIFICATION AS A GENERAL PERSPECTIVE ON COST ANALYSIS

The problems that cost analysts and estimators solve very often can be described in this way: Given information about the performance of a certain system in response to specified inputs, and information about a new input for the system, how will the system respond to the new inputs?

For example, suppose the task is to estimate the cost of manufacturing a new radio. As data, an analyst will have observed costs of manufacturing other radios, the characteristics of those radios and the way in which they were manufactured, and information about the characteristics of the new radios and plans for their manufacture.

Here, the "system" is the industry that produces radios, if the manufacturer is not known. If the manufacturer is known, the system is that producer's plant and set of suppliers. The system performance of interest is, of course, the cost of producing radios.

The specified inputs are the characteristics of the existing radios, the sequences of lots in which they were produced, and, probably, the dates during which they were made. The new inputs are the same data for the new radio.

An important branch of the engineering discipline called mathematical system theory treats such problems. Known as "system identification," it is the subject of many books[1] and a great many papers. The recent literature has some explicit applications of methods from system identification to cost analysis.[2]

Figure 1 shows the general system identification paradigm:

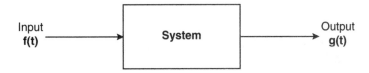

Figure 1. The System Identification Paradigm

Given the input $f(t)$, and output $g(t)$, one is to predict the system's output to a new input, say, $g_1(t)$.

System identification methods are broadly classified as "parametric" and "nonparametric." In this language, a parametric identification method is one in which the unknown system is characterized by a set of parameters, which are to be determined from the data.

Cost analysts regularly practice parametric system identification. For example, determining theoretical first-unit cost T_1 and exponent b of a power-law cost-progress curve

---

[1] Here are some examples: *System Identification*, by Sage, A. P. and J. L. Melsa, Academic Press, New York, 1971; *Feedback Systems: Input-Output Properties*, by De Soer, C. and M. Vidyasagar, Academic Press, New York, 1975; Maybeck, P. S., *Stochastic Models, Estimation, and Control*, Volume 2, Academic Press, New York, 1982; and *Applied Non-Linear Control*, by Slotine, J. J. and W. Li, Prentice-Hall, New York, 1991.

[2] Gallagher, M. A., and D. A. Lee, "Final-Cost Estimates for Research & Development Programs Conditioned on Realized Costs," *Military Operations Research*, Volume 2, Number 2, pp. 51-68, 1996.

(learning curve), given costs of a few lots, is an exercise of this kind. Here the "time" parameter is the sequence of lot indices, the input $f(t)$ is the sequence of lot sizes, or, equivalently, the sequence $\{L_i, U_i\}$ of lot-starting quantities L_i, and end quantities U_i. The output $g(t)$ is the corresponding sequence of lot costs C_i.

The parametric model of the system is the power-law cost-progress curve,

$$C_i = T_1 \sum_{j=L_i}^{U_i} j^b \qquad (1)$$

Cost analysts often use the least-squares method of determining the parameters T_1 and b, i.e.,

$$\min_{T_1, b} \sum_{1}^{M} \left[\tilde{C}_i - T_1 \sum_{j=L_i}^{U_i} j^b \right]^2 \qquad (2)$$

where $\tilde{C}_i$ denotes the observed cost of lot i. This method also is a standard method of parametric system identification.

The tools of system identification offer many parametric methods that are directly useful to cost analysts. Footnote 2, for example, applies a method of parametric system identification called multiple-model adaptive estimation (MMAE) that develops statistics of the estimated parameters, conditioned on a sequence of observations.

Also, system identification methods include a class known as nonparametric methods. In this kind of system identification, an unknown function is not characterized by a small number of parameters, but, rather, is to be determined as a function, by methods appropriate to that task. For example, if the unknown system is linear; causal (outputs are due solely to inputs); and time-independent (a given input, made when the system is in a specific state always gives the same output), then there is a (possibly generalized) function **h(t)**, such that, when the system initially has output zero, the output **g(t)** is related to the input **f(t)** by

$$g(t) = \int_0^t h(t-\tau)f(\tau)d\tau \qquad (3)$$

The function **h(t)**, which is called the system's impulse response, characterizes the system's input-output relation fully. If we know **h(t)**, we can use (3) to predict the response **g(t)** to any input **f(t)**.

We may identify the system from observations by solving an appropriate mathematical problem to determine **h(t)**. For example, suppose we are given a specific input $f_0(t)$ and the corresponding output $g_0(t)$. By a straightforward change of the integration variable, (3) implies

$$\int_0^t f(t-\tau)h(\tau)d\tau = g(t) \qquad (4)$$

Since (4) holds for the given input-output pair $f_0 - g_0$, it implies the first-kind Volterra integral equation

$$\int_0^t f_0(t-\tau)h(\tau)d\tau = g_0(t) \qquad (5)$$

for **h(t)**. We may solve (5) by standard methods to determine the function **h**, and then use the result to predict the system's response for other inputs.[3]

---

[3]The numerical analysis of this process, and the nature and effects of errors in the resulting approximations for **h(t)**, is actually somewhat complex. See Lee, D. A. and Audley, D., "Ill Posed and Well Posed Problems in System Identification," *IEEE Transactions on Automatic Control*, AC-19, pp. 738 et seq., 1974.

We mention an opportunity for this kind of nonparametric system identification in our work in Chapter 5 on Rayleigh methods for development estimates.

The term "nonparametric system identification" is unfortunate for cost analysts. Generally, they refer to estimates made on the basis of a fairly small set of descriptive parameters as "parametric cost estimates." They refer to estimates made by attempts to build up an estimate of system cost from detailed estimates of the costs of all its parts as "nonparametric cost estimates."

Applications of system identification methods to estimate costs of complete systems or of major system components, always will be "parametric cost estimates," even when they are made by the methods of nonparametric system identification.

Particularly when faced with a challenging task, in which a thorough understanding of the uncertainties in the estimate is important, the cost analyst may get a good deal of help from methods of system identification already developed by people working with mathematical system theory.

CHAPTER 2

THE NATURE OF COST-PROGRESS CURVES

As more and more units of an item are produced in a given plant, the cost of producing a unit generally decreases.[4,5,6,7] (Please note that we speak here of changes with increasing total production in a *given* plant, which occur even for production at a constant rate. These changes thus are not simply economies of scale.) Figure 2 shows an example of this relationship. It is for production of a complex item—a tactical missile. Two or three thousand missiles were made in a typical lot and about 20,000 missiles were produced in total.

Figure 2 also illustrates the way cost analysts traditionally graph production cost data. The average cost of each production lot is plotted against a representative value of the cumulative production quantity achieved during the lot (we will discuss just how to compute that value in Chapter 3). Both axes have logarithmic scales.

The decreasing-cost phenomenon itself is called "cost progress" and the cost-quantity relation for a given

---

[4]Wright, T. P., "Factors Affecting the Cost of Airplanes," *Journal of Aerospace Science*, Volume 3, pp. 122–128, 1936.

[5]Moses, O. D., "Extensions to the Cost Progress Model: An Analysis of Factors Influencing Unit Cost of Weapon Systems," *Journal of Cost Analysis*, to appear.

[6]Yelle, L. E., "The Learning Curve: Historical Review and Comprehensive Survey," *Decision Sciences*, Volume 10, pp. 302–327, 1979.

[7]Dutton, J. M., A. Thomas, and J. Butler, "The History of Cost Progress Functions as a Managerial Technology," *Business History Review*, Volume 58, pp. 204–233, 1984.

production exercise is known as the "cost-progress curve," or "learning curve," of the exercise.

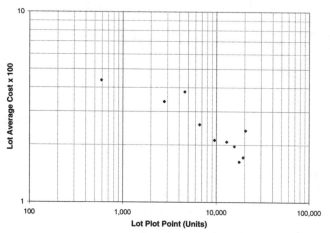

Figure 2. An Observed Cost-Progress Curve

In this chapter, we introduce the traditional cost analyst's models and descriptive terms for cost-progress curves. We will then discuss the nature of the cost-progress phenomenon. We will see that analyzing manufacturers' incentives to make items less expensive to produce, and to make their plants more efficient, gives helpful means of predicting the sorts of cost-progress curves that will be seen in specific cases.

COST-PROGRESS MODELS

Cost analysts use several models of cost progress. Those most commonly used are the cumulative average model and the unit model.

The cumulative average model often is called the Wright model for T. P. Wright, who in 1936 published the first comprehensive paper on cost-progress curves.[8] This model is:

$$A(Q) = A_1 Q^b \qquad (6)$$

where $A(Q)$ is the average cost of the first Q units; A_1 and b are constants.

The unit model, often called the Crawford model after the man who first described it carefully, is

$$C(Q) = T_1 Q^b \qquad (7)$$

where $C(Q)$ is the cost of the Qth unit; T_1 and b are constants.

The data of Figure 2 can be interpreted as scattering about a straight line on the log-log plot. This behavior is typical of cost-progress curves—and that fact is used to justify the power-law forms of (1) and (7).

BASIC DESCRIPTIVE PARAMETERS: EXPONENT AND SLOPE

Cost analysts have traditional names for the constants in (6) and (7). The constants A_1 and T_1 are both known as the "theoretical first-unit cost." (Actually, it is traditional to use the symbol T_1 for both of them, but it seems more clear to use distinct symbols.)

These names make sense: in the unit model, the unit cost for $Q = 1$ would be T_1. In the cumulative average model, the cumulative average cost of one unit would be A_1, since the average cost of the first 1 units is just the cost of the first unit.

---

[8]Wright, T. P., l. c. ante.

Thus, A_1 is indeed the cost of the first unit. Referring to T_1 and A_1 as theoretical first-unit costs emphasizes the fact that these are the costs of the first unit in a model of the actual production process and not necessarily the actual cost of the first unit produced. Very often, the best fit of either a unit model or a cumulative average model to data for a production process will have a T_1 or A_1 quite different from the observed cost of the first unit.

The parameter **b** of either model is known as the "exponent" of the curve. Closely related to the exponent is the quantity known as the "slope" of the curve represented by (1) or (7). For both models, when quantity doubles, the modeled cost decreases by a specific ratio; this ratio is what cost analysts call the slope of the curve. To be precise, the cost analyst's slope **S** is defined by

$$S \equiv \frac{\text{Cost at quantity } 2Q}{\text{Cost at quantity } Q} \qquad (8)$$

Straightforward algebra shows that, for both models, the cost analyst's slope **S** is related to the exponent **b** by

$$S = 2^b \qquad (9)$$

Traditionally, slopes are expressed as percentages.

Note that the slope is not the same as the geometric slopes $\dfrac{dC}{dQ}$ or $\dfrac{dA}{dQ}$. For the Crawford model, exponent **b** is the logarithmic derivative of **C(Q)**, the limiting value of the relative change in **C** to the relative change in **Q**:

$$b = \lim_{\Delta Q \to 0} \left| \frac{\frac{\Delta C}{C}}{\frac{\Delta Q}{Q}} \right| = \frac{d(\ln(C))}{d(\ln(Q))} = \frac{Q}{C} \frac{dC}{dQ} \qquad (10)$$

It follows from (9) and (10) that the cost analyst's slope **S** is related to the geometric slope $\frac{dC}{dQ}$ by

$$S = 2^{\frac{Q}{C} \frac{dC}{dQ}} \qquad (11)$$

Expressions for the exponent and cost analyst's slope in the Wright model follow from (10) and (11) when **A(Q)** replaces **C(Q)**. From now on, we will refer to the cost analyst's slope simply as "slope."

The definitions of exponent and slope came from the specific Wright and Crawford models of cost progress. For these forms of **C(Q)** and **A(Q)**, slope and exponent both have constant values for all **Q**.

Cost-progress functions **C(Q)** do not necessarily follow either the Wright or the Crawford model exactly, however. In many if not most cases, no single Wright or Crawford curve fits the data exactly over all quantities.

Cost analysts still speak of the slope of these more general cost-progress curves. For such curves, slope and exponent are functions of quantity. Equations (10) and (11) are the definitions of the local exponent and local slope of a general Crawford cost-progress curve **C(Q)**; replacing **C(Q)** with **A(Q)** defines these quantities for Wright curves.

Cost analysts speak of cost-progress curves for which unit costs drop sharply with increasing quantity as having "steep" slopes. Thus, the smaller the value of **S**, the steeper the slope.

The slope increases as the magnitude of the geometric slope increases at a fixed value of **Q/C**, as one sees from (11).

EXTENDED MODELS OF COST PROGRESS

Extensions to the basic cumulative average and unit models incorporate other features of production, as well as quantity. Production rate is probably the additional feature most commonly modeled. An expanded unit model is often used for this, in the form

$$C(Q) = T_1 Q^b R^c \qquad \textbf{(12)}$$

where **R** denotes production rate, i.e., the number of units produced in a production period, and **T$_1$**, **b**, and **c** are constants. The parameter **c** is called the rate exponent of the curve, and the quantity 2^c is known as the curve's rate slope. When it is necessary to distinguish it from the rate slope, the quantity 2^b is called the curve's quantity slope. Like quantity slopes, rate slopes are traditionally expressed as percentages.

Equations (6), (7), and (12) are all *ad hoc* models of complex processes. Before discussing their use, we should give some thought to the basic economic reasons for the cost-progress phenomenon. The results will give us helpful means to predict the kind of cost-progress curves that will be seen for specific production cases.

WHY COST PROGRESS?

Once a production plant is set up, unit costs may decrease because

- Production workers become more experienced, and so more efficient, as they make more units.

- Designers refine the product so that units can be made at less cost.

- Industrial engineers improve the production processes.

- Buyers find cheaper sources of materials.

All but the first of these reasons for cost progress are things that do not happen automatically as more units are produced. Rather, they are results of investments in productivity and in production technology. (We may consider employing energetic buyers who seek lower-cost supplies—as opposed to clerks who merely order repeatedly from the same suppliers—an investment in production technology.)

Management controls these investments. So, to understand cost progress, we need to understand the economic incentives that cause managers to make them.

To gain some insight into these incentives, let's suppose that in a given plant, the unit cost **C** of a product is given by

$$C = f(I) \tag{13}$$

where **I** is the total investment in producibility and production technology. Let's further suppose that **f(I)** satisfies some common-sense conditions:

- **f(I)** is monotone nonincreasing and bounded below (production costs should not get larger when investments are made to reduce them, and unit cost cannot be made arbitrarily small).

- **f(I)** is continuously differentiable, and **f'(I)** is monotone increasing, bounded above by 0. (The differentiability condition is, I admit, for mathematical convenience. The following discussion can be carried through under much weaker regularity assumptions, for example, the requirement that **f(I)** has at most a finite number of finite-jump discontinuities. To do so seems to war with simple explanations of the basic ideas, however. Monotonicity of the derivative builds in diminishing returns: as costs decrease, driving them down by a given amount requires more investment.)

To have a specific example of such a function, we may take[9]

$$f(I) = C_{min} + \Delta e^{-\alpha I} \qquad (14)$$

Now, let's reckon the manufacturer's profit **P**, including costs and benefits of investments in producibility and production technology. Let the unit price in production period **i** be p_i, and let the producibility-production technology investment in that period be δ_i. For simplicity, let's assume that all production lots have the same size **N**, which is the efficient lot size for the plant.[10] Then

---

[9] This choice of **f(I)** is not entirely arbitrary. It follows from a simple, linear diminishing-returns model for the payoff of investments in producibility and production technology, i.e.,

$$\frac{dC}{dt} = -\alpha p(t)(C - C_{min}); \; C(0) = C_{min} + \Delta$$

In this model, **p(t)** is the rate of expenditure on producibility and production technology, **C_min** is the minimum cost of producing a unit, and Δ is the amount by which the starting unit cost exceeds that minimum value. The parameter α, which has the dimensions of ($)^{-1}$, is a constant. Standard methods of solving this initial value problem lead to (14). Alternatively, it is easy to verify by differentiation and evaluation for t = 0 that C = f(I(t)) satisfies the initial value problem.

[10] We are considering managers' incentives to make producibility-production technology investments in an existing plant, designed to produce at a rate **N**, which is certain to sell at the prices p_i. This is an idealized model of the environment in which some major weapon systems are produced. (See LMI Report PA902T1, May 2000.)

$$P = \left\{ \left[N(p_0 - f(0)) - \delta_0 \right] + \left[N(p_1 - f(\delta_0)) - \delta_1 \right] + \left[N(p_2 - f(\delta_0 + \delta_1)) - \delta_2 \right] \right.$$

$$\text{(15)}$$

$$\left. + \left[N(p_{M-1} - f(\delta_0 + \delta_1 + ... + \delta_{M-2})) - \delta_{M-1} \right] + \left[N(p_M - f(\delta_0 + \delta_1 + ... + \delta_{M-1})) \right] \right\}$$

We may expect the producer to choose the string of investments $\{\delta_0, \delta_1, ..., \delta_{M-1}\}$ to maximize **P**, in view of other aspects of the business environment in which the items are produced. Certainly, any relation between production costs and price will be an important feature of that environment. Let's consider the investments that would be incentivized by two cases of this relation.

PRICE LOOSELY COUPLED TO COST

If prices are essentially determined by features of the business environment other than production cost, and if the producer is uncertain whether production will continue past any given year, then presumably the manufacturer will choose producibility-production technology investments to minimize total cost for each production period. In this case, the manufacturer will choose the **i**th period's investment δ_i to solve

$$\min_{\delta_i} \left[Nf(I_i + \delta_i) + \delta_i \right] \qquad \text{(16)}$$

where I_i is the total investment for the periods preceding period **i**.

If the optimization problem (16) were unconstrained, then its solution of would be the value of δ_i that solves

$$Nf'(I_i + \delta_i) + 1 = 0 \qquad \text{(17)}$$

that is, δ_i would be chosen as the investment needed to drive total investment to the value I^*, given by

$$I^* \equiv (f')^{-1}(-1/N) \qquad (18)$$

We will refer to I^* as the "maximum efficient investment."

In reality, there are limits to the producibility-production technology investment that a given plant can absorb in one production period; for example, it takes time to redesign the product and to implement improved production technology. Other factors that limit per-period investment are capital rationing, and the need for someone to notice production line inefficiencies and to invent remedies. Consequently, the maximum efficient investment I^* cannot in general be reached in one production period, and minimization (16) is subject to the constraint

$$\delta_i \leq \delta_{max} \qquad (19)$$

If the constraint (19) were not active, then the solution of (16) would be the value of δ_i that satisfies (17), i.e.,

$$\delta_i = (f')^{-1}(-1/N) - I_i \qquad (20)$$

Our assumptions on the function $f(I)$ are sufficient to guarantee the existence of the inverse function $(f')^{-1}$. In general, the solution of (16) subject to (19) is

$$\delta_i = \begin{cases} \min \begin{cases} (f')^{-1}(-1/N) - I_i \\ \delta_{max} \end{cases} & \text{when } (f')^{-1}(-1/N) > I_i \quad (21) \\ 0, & \text{otherwise} \end{cases}$$

For the specific function $f(I) = C_{min} + \Delta e^{-\alpha I}$, (21) leads to

$$\delta_i = \begin{cases} \min \left\{ \begin{array}{l} \dfrac{1}{\alpha}\ln(N\alpha\Delta) - I_i \\[2ex] \delta_{max} \end{array} \right\} & \text{when } \dfrac{1}{\alpha}\ln(N\alpha\Delta) > I_i \\[3ex] 0, & \text{otherwise} \end{cases} \qquad (22)$$

The sequence of incremental investments δ_i, determined by (21) for the general case or by (22) for our particular choice of $f(I)$, maps directly into a sequence of total investments I_i. This investment sequence then maps into a sequence of unit costs $f(I_i)$. (For our example, $f(I_i) = C_{min} + \Delta e^{-\alpha I_i}$.) This last sequence is, of course, the cost-progress curve.

The optimal sequence of investments determined by (21) or (22) typically begins with several periods at the maximum investment δ_{max}. Eventually, if production continues long enough, the cumulative investment I_i becomes large enough that, in some period i_{flat}, an investment less than δ_{max} brings the cumulative investment to the maximum efficient investment $I^* = \dfrac{1}{\alpha}\ln(N\alpha\Delta)$. (Provided $N\alpha\Delta > 1$; later, we will deal with the contrary case in the section "Small Lots and Limited Per-Period Reductions.") At this point, because of the exponential character of the particular $f(I)$ that we are using as an example, further investments in producibility and production technology do not yield greater profits, so no further investments are made, and the cost-progress curve becomes flat. For example, Figure 3 shows the first 14 points of a cost-progress curve of this kind, plotted in the cost analyst's traditional way. The points shown are for the first lot through the lot after the one that results in the lowest unit cost, i.e., lot number $i_{flat} + 1$.

The cost-progress curve of Figure 3 is very much like curves actually observed. An experienced cost analyst's description of that curve might well be something like, "Well, they started out a little flat, but by the third lot they'd settled into a very commendable 70 percent curve. Then, as often happens, they flattened out again for the last three lots."

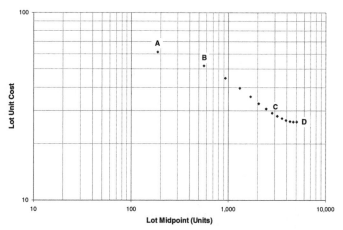

Figure 3. A Theoretical Cost-Progress Curve

The purpose of this material is not to argue that the specific model we are using as an illustrative example is necessarily the "right" one. Rather, the idea is to show that arguments from economic principles can generate cost-progress curves not at all unlike those observed.

PARAMETERS OF THE THEORETICAL COST-PROGRESS CURVES

Even though the present model is not a very sophisticated one, its properties can give us useful indications of the ways plant and production processes affect cost-progress curves. The curves generated by our example, as illustrated in Figure 3, have four salient features, noted as A, B, C, and D. The first of these is an initial, relatively flat portion, shown between points A and B. The curve steepens with increasing quantity until, at point C, it achieves its steepest slope. As quantity increases beyond the quantity of point C, the curve flattens, slowly at first, and then abruptly as the maximal effective investment $I^* = \dfrac{1}{\alpha}\ln(N\alpha\Delta)$ is reached. This is point D on Figure 3.

These four features of the curves generated by our example are characterized by three nondimensional parameters: $\dfrac{\Delta}{C_{min}}$, $\alpha\delta_{max}$, and $N\alpha\Delta$. The ratio $\dfrac{\Delta}{C_{min}}$ is a "headroom" parameter, indicating how much opportunity the given plant provides for investments in producibility and production technology to drive unit costs down. As we will see, the product $\alpha\delta_{max}$ describes the degree to which unit costs can be driven down by investments in producibility and production technology in a single production period. Finally, at lot number i_{flat},

$$i_{flat} \approx \frac{\ln(N\alpha D)}{\alpha\delta_{max}} \qquad (23)$$

investment reaches the largest efficient value and the curve becomes flat.

We now need to complete two analyses: one to explain the nature of $\alpha\delta_{max}$ and one to relate the maximum slope point to the three parameters. The first of these is straightforward: the differential equation of Footnote 9 may be written

$$\frac{d(C - C_{min})}{C - C_{min}} = -\alpha p\, dt \qquad (24)$$

Integrating (24) over one production period, from t_i to t_{i+1}, gives

$$\ln\frac{C_{i+1} - C_{min}}{C_i - C_{min}} = -\alpha \int_{t_i}^{t_{i+1}} p(t)\, dt = -\alpha\delta_{max} \qquad (25)$$

when the maximum per-period investment is applied. The logarithm in (25) is approximately equal to the relative change in $C - C_{min}$ between lot i and lot $i + 1$. This fact establishes $\alpha\delta_{max}$ as the maximum size of this relative change.

The parameter $\alpha\delta_{max}$ typically governs the behavior of the cost-progress curve for the first few lots (points A and B in Figure 3). To see this, we consider the local behavior of our theoretical curves.

Referring to (10), we may define a "segment exponent" b_{si} of the line segment connecting points (C_i, Q_i) and (C_{i+1}, Q_{i+1}) as

$$b_{si} = \frac{\ln(C_{i+1}) - \ln(C_i)}{\ln(Q_{i+1}) - \ln(Q_i)} = \frac{\ln(C_{i+1} / C_i)}{\ln(Q_{i+1} / Q_i)} \qquad (26)$$

We may regard the quantity $S_{si} \equiv 2^{b_{si}}$ as the cost-progress curve slope associated with the ith segment.

When, as is typically true, $\dfrac{\Delta}{C_{min}} \gg 1$ and $\alpha\delta_{max} \ll 1$, the segment slopes S_{si} of the early lots, i.e., those for which $1 < i \ll 1/\alpha\delta_{max}$, are given approximately by

$$S_{si} \approx 2^{-i\alpha\delta_{max}} = e^{-i\alpha\delta_{max}\ln 2} \approx 1 - 0.69 i\alpha\delta_{max} \qquad (27)$$

Thus, the segment slopes of early lots start flat when $\alpha\delta_{max} \ll 1$ and steadily steepen. For example, if $\alpha\delta_{max} = 0.05$, then the initial segment slopes are approximately 98, 93, and 89 percent. For larger values of $\alpha\delta_{max}$, say around 0.2, the initial segments are not so flat—they begin in the mid-eighties of percentages—and they steepen rapidly. These considerations show how $\alpha\delta_{max}$, which represents the maximum relative per-period change in $C - C_{min}$, governs the behavior of the cost-progress curve for early lots, like those of points A and B in Figure 3.

Now, let's investigate the maximum-slope point (point C in Figure 3). We do so by analyzing (26), to find the segment at which the segment slope is steepest (has its smallest value) and the value of the steepest segment slope.

So long as lot number i_{flat} has not been reached, at each production period the profit-maximizing manufacturer will invest δ_{max} in producibility and production technology. For the ith such period, for the unit-cost function $f(I)$ of (14), we will thus find

$$C_i = C_{min} + \Delta e^{-i\alpha\delta_{max}} \qquad (28)$$

In our simple model the total quantity at lot i is iN. It follows that the steepest segment slope will correspond to the solution of

$$\min_i \frac{\ln\left(\dfrac{C_{min} + \Delta e^{-(i+1)\alpha\delta_{max}}}{C_{min} + \Delta e^{-i\alpha\delta_{max}}}\right)}{\ln\left(\dfrac{i+1}{i}\right)} \qquad (29)$$

Assuming that $\dfrac{\Delta}{C_{min}}$ is large compared with one, that $\alpha\delta_{max}$ is small compared with one, and that the minimizing value i^* of i is large compared with one, so that $\dfrac{C_{min}}{\Delta}e^{i\alpha\delta}$ is comparable to one brings (29) to the form

$$\min_{x} \frac{x}{1 + \dfrac{C_{min}}{\Delta} e^x} \tag{30}$$

where $x \equiv i\alpha\delta_{max}$.

Unfortunately, it seems that the solution of even the simplified minimization problem cannot be expressed readily in terms of known functions. Numerical experiments indicate that the steepest slope is often found at values of i for which $e^{-i\alpha\delta_{max}} \approx \dfrac{C_{min}}{\Delta}$. A crude approximate solution of (30), obtained by taking one iteration of Newton's method after a first guess of $x = \ln\left(\dfrac{\Delta}{C_{min}}\right)$, leads to

$$i^* = \frac{1}{\alpha\delta_{max}}\left[r + \frac{2-r}{r}\right] \tag{31}$$

where $r \equiv \ln\left(\dfrac{\Delta}{C_{min}}\right)$. The corresponding approximate value of the minimal segment exponent b^*_{si} is

$$b^*_{si} = -\frac{r + \dfrac{2-r}{r}}{1 + e^{\frac{2-r}{r}}} \tag{32}$$

If $\dfrac{2-r}{r}$ is small compared with one, then (32) leads to

$$b^*_{si} = -\frac{r}{2} \tag{33}$$

In this approximation, the steepest segment slope S^*_{si} has a particularly simple value:

$$S_{si} = 2^{b^*_{si}} \approx e^{-\frac{r}{2}\ln(2)} = e^{-0.347r} \approx \left(\frac{C_{min}}{\Delta}\right)^{\frac{1}{3}} \qquad (34)$$

While crude, approximations (31) through (34) do give helpful information about the steepest slope point of our theoretical curve. Equation (31) shows that i^* is a slowly increasing function of $\frac{\Delta}{C_{min}}$ for fixed $\alpha\delta_{max}$ and that, for fixed $\frac{\Delta}{C_{min}}$, i^* is roughly proportional to $\frac{1}{\alpha\delta_{max}}$. Equation (34) is a helpful guide to the value of the steepest segment slope, showing that, like i^*, it is a slowly varying function of $\frac{\Delta}{C_{min}}$.

Relatively large values of the headroom ratio $\frac{\Delta}{C_{min}}$, say, those greater than 2, are associated with small values of the steepest slopes, in the 70 percent range. For example, in approximation (34), a headroom parameter of 2.5 leads to a 73 percent maximum slope.

RELATING THEORETICAL COST-PROGRESS CURVE PARAMETERS TO FEATURES OF PRODUCT AND PLANT

Armed with the understanding we've gained about the way its parameters affect our theoretical cost-progress curves, we can relate features of production situations to the curves. Production of complex, expensive items like airplanes and tactical missiles in large plants tends to have relatively large values of $\frac{\Delta}{C_{min}}$. This happens because the item's complexity tends to discourage both thorough optimization of designs for producibility during development, and large-scale automation of production. Consequently, plants typically come on-line with many opportunities to improve both producibility and production technology. Thus, manufacturing such items generally leads to reasonably steep slopes.

The maximum-improvement parameter $\alpha\delta_{max}$ also tends to be relatively large in these cases because the complex production facility affords many opportunities for adjustments—and its large size generally means that there will be enough people to develop and implement several changes in one production period. In the context of our discussion, this leads one to expect that cost-progress curves for manufacturing expensive, complex items will *not* have a long, initial flat segment.

Some complex, expensive items, such as tactical missiles, are made in large lots and in substantial total quantities. This implies that lot number **i*** is likely to be reached, so that the steepest segment slope is likely to be seen, and also, that flattening at later lots is distinctly possible.

Other complex, expensive items, say, bombers, are likely to be made in somewhat smaller lots than are tactical missiles; their total production quantity tends to be smaller. Accordingly, cost-progress curves for these items may not realize the steepest segment slope and may not exhibit any flattening at later lots.

By contrast to production of airplanes and tactical missiles, production of relatively simple items—whose designs can be thoroughly optimized, such as electronic equipment with narrow functions (like radios or munitions) for which substantially automated production is feasible—are likely to have small headroom ratios. Their relatively people-less plants probably cannot absorb enough producibility-production technology investment to give much relative change per period in the difference between minimum and current production unit costs, $C - C_{min}$. Also, they tend to be made in large total quantities, likely to be larger than i_{flat}. For such a case, the model we are exploring would predict a less steeply sloping cost-progress curve overall, with noticeable flattening at larger quantities. Figure 4 shows an example of just such a flat curve.

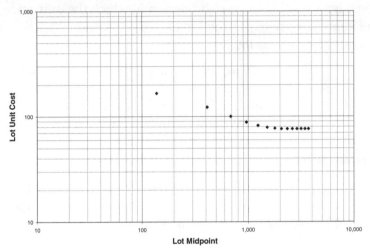

Figure 4. Cost-Progress Curve with Limited Headroom and Flattening

So far, we've developed some ideas about how features of plant and product can affect cost progress when the business environment leads to minimizing production cost in each period. The ideas may be used to get qualitative estimates of the cost-progress curves to be expected in specific cases.

The environment does not necessarily conduce to minimizing production cost in each period in all cases, however. In the next section we consider another possibility.

PRICE CLOSELY COUPLED TO COST

In some cases, the manufacturer agrees to disclose production costs, and prices are set as a specified function of cost. Such arrangements are common in manufacturing major weapon systems.

To see the producer's incentives in these cases, let's consider a specific price-cost relation in which the unit price of the items in a given production lot are proportional to the unit cost of the previous lot:

$$p_{i+1} = (1+\gamma)C_i \qquad (35)$$

Let us also assume that none of the investments in producibility and production technology may be counted in the C_i. After a bit of algebra, one finds that, for this case, the manufacturer's profit on a set of **m** lots is

$$P = N\gamma\left[f(0) + f(\delta_0) + f(\delta_0 + \delta_1) + \ldots + f(\delta_0 + \delta_1 + \delta_2 + \ldots + \delta_{m-2})\right]$$

$$- \left[Nf(\delta_0 + \delta_1 + \delta_2 + \ldots + \delta_{m-1}) + (\delta_0 + \delta_1 + \delta_2 + \ldots + \delta_{m-1})\right] \qquad (36)$$

As for the previous cost-price relation, here too, the manufacturer will choose the sequence of investments that maximizes **P**. The solution is obvious in one case: according to (36), **P** is the sum of a positive term and a negative term. **P** will be maximal when the positive term is as large as possible and the negative term is as small as possible. Recalling that **f(I)** is nondecreasing, we see that the positive term will be as large as possible if the manufacturer makes *no investments at all* through period (**m** – 2). If

$$\frac{1}{\alpha}\ln(N\alpha\Delta) \leq \delta_{max}, \qquad (37)$$

then by a single investment in the last period for which investment is possible, period $(m-1)$, the manufacturer can make the negative term in (36) as small as possible. Consequently, the sequence of investments $\{0, 0, 0, ..., \delta_{max}\}$ is optimal.

The resulting cost-progress curve is $\{C_{min} + \Delta, C_{min} + \Delta, ..., C_{min} + 1/\alpha\}$. It is utterly flat for all but the last lot. This is certainly different from the curve that the incentives of the previous section would have produced.

While valid only when inequality (37) holds, the result illustrates what happens in general under the present incentives. The manufacturer will make investments as late as possible, although perhaps in earlier lots than the last one. The resulting cost-progress curves imply greater total costs than those resulting under other incentives, such as those of the section above, "Price Loosely Coupled to Cost."

The two cases we have considered—prices essentially uncoupled from production cost and prices tightly coupled to production cost—are polar cases of the business environment's impact on cost progress. Other cases are well worth considering: some part of producibility-production technology investments may be counted in cost, for the purpose of reckoning prices; and discounting and regulatory lag may play a role in the manufacturer's incentives. Rogerson[11] treats some of these.

---

[11]Rogerson, W., "Regulatory Lag, Incentives for Process Innovation and the Defense Procurement Process," Lecture Notes, Department of Economics, Northwestern University, November 1992.

SMALL LOTS AND LIMITED PER-PERIOD REDUCTIONS

We will consider just one more case in our set of illustrative examples. In both the previous sections, we dealt only with cases in which the minimum value of the sum of lot costs and investment was positive, i.e., for which $(f')^{-1}(-1/N) > 0$ in the general case, or $N\alpha\Delta > 1$ for the specific $f(I)$ that we have considered.

Now, $N\alpha\Delta = N\,\alpha\delta_{max}\,\dfrac{\Delta}{\delta_{max}}$. We have seen that $\alpha\delta_{max}$ represents the maximum per-period relative change in $C - C_{min}$. Typically, $\alpha\delta_{max}$ is not larger than a few tens of percentages. The parameter Δ represents a change in unit cost, and so it is likely to be smaller than the overall maximum producibility-production technology investment δ_{max}. Accordingly, to have $N\alpha\Delta > 1$, N must be sufficiently large—generally substantially greater than one.

But that may not always happen. Satellites, in particular, have been built essentially as single units. For these cases—for both of the business environments considered in the preceding two sections—the result would be that the manufacturer has no incentive to make investments in producibility or production technology. Our work would, accordingly, lead us to expect little learning, and that is in fact what has been observed for satellites.

Even if N is larger than one, sufficiently small values of $\alpha\delta_{max}$ and $\dfrac{\Delta}{\delta_{max}}$ may still bring a production exercise into the case covered by this section.

SUMMARY

In this chapter, we considered the cost-progress phenomenon and saw the conventional models that cost analysts use to describe it. We also explored the way that business environments, and the nature of the product and of the manufacturing plant, create incentives that, arguably, determine the cost progress that a given production exercise will exhibit. Next, we discuss the tasks for which cost analysts use cost-progress models.

CHAPTER 3

THE USE OF COST-PROGRESS CURVES

Cost analysts use models of the cost-progress phenomenon for several tasks. These include:

- Estimate the total cost of manufacturing all planned production, given the costs of a few initial lots.

- Estimate the lot-by-lot costs of a given buy pattern (sequence of lot sizes), given the costs of a few lots of another buy pattern.

- Estimate the lot-by-lot costs of a given buy pattern, given an estimate for the cost of an initial set of units (typically, an initial lot) and an estimate of the appropriate learning curve slope.

Except for the last one, these tasks typically require an analyst to estimate the parameters of a cost-progress curve model from the observed costs and known quantities of a set of lots. In this chapter, we discuss ways of doing that parameter estimation and we apply the results to some examples of the tasks described above.

SOME MATHEMATICAL PRELIMINARIES

We'll find it convenient to collect some standard mathematical relations in one place, before starting the work of this chapter. In the subsections below, we do just that.

LOT COSTS FOR WRIGHT AND CRAWFORD COST-PROGRESS MODELS

We will continually need expressions for the costs of the lot that starts with unit **L**, and ends with unit **U**. With the Wright model,

$$A(Q) = A_1 Q^b \tag{38}$$

or

$$\frac{1}{Q} \sum_{j=1}^{Q} C(j) = A_1 Q^b \tag{39}$$

and so the cost of the first **Q** items is

$$\sum_{j=1}^{Q} C(j) = A_1 Q^{b+1} \tag{40}$$

Since the cost $C_{L,U}$ of the lot that runs from unit **L** through unit **U** is the cost of the first **U** units minus the cost of the first $(L-1)$ units, with the Wright model,

$$C_{L,U} = A_1 \left[U^{b+1} - (L-1)^{b+1} \right] \tag{41}$$

With the Crawford model,

$$C(Q) = T_1 Q^b \tag{42}$$

and we can evaluate $C_{L,U}$ directly as

$$C_{L,U} = T_1 \sum_{Q=L}^{Q=U} j^b \tag{43}$$

PLOT POINTS

Using the Crawford model, it is conventional to associate the cost $C_{L,U}$ with the lot "plot point" $\bar{x}_{L,U}$ at which the unit cost of the Crawford model is equal to the average cost of the units in the lot. Thus

$$T_1\left(\bar{x}_{L,U}\right)^b = \frac{T_1}{U-L+1} \sum_L^U j^b \qquad (44)$$

which leads to

$$\bar{x}_{L,U}(b) = \left(\frac{1}{U-L+1} \sum_L^U j^b\right)^{\frac{1}{b}} \qquad (45)$$

When using the Wright model, one generally deals with sequences of values of average cost $A(Q)$ for several values of Q. It is natural to plot $A(Q)$ at quantity Q.

CRAWFORD MODEL LOT COSTS AND THE ASHER FUNCTION

There is no simple, exact expression in terms of familiar functions for the sums of powers of integers $\sum_L^U j^b$ that one must treat when using Crawford curves. Among his many contributions to cost analysis, Harold Asher[12] suggested, and motivated very clearly, the approximation

---

[12]Asher, H., *Cost-Quantity Relationships in the Airframe Industry*, RAND, Santa Monica, 1956, p. 36.

$$\sum_{L}^{U} j^b \approx \frac{1}{1+b}\left[(U+0.5)^{1+b}-(L-0.5)^{1+b}\right] \qquad (46)$$

Cost analysts frequently neglect the 0.5 terms in (46) and use the crude approximation

$$\sum_{L}^{U} j^b \approx \frac{1}{1+b}\left(U^{1+b}-L^{1+b}\right) \qquad (47)$$

Approximations like (46) or (47) were helpful—indeed, necessary—when cost analysts had no computing aids but mechanical calculators, slide rules, and graph paper. They may still be useful for rough work.

They can also cause trouble when people forget that they are only approximations. Attempting to use (47) to evaluate the cost of the Nth unit, setting $L = U = N$, gives a dreadfully wrong result! (I once witnessed a heated argument that came about from an inadvertent use of (47) in just this way.) Approximation (46), while better, is still wrong when used to evaluate $C(j)$, and wasteful of computing power.

Fortunately, today all serious practitioners have plenty of computerized support. Now, we need ways to generate accurate numerical values of $\sum_{L}^{U} j^b$ efficiently, rather than ways to approximate the sum.

Simply coding $\sum_{L}^{U} j^b$ in most programming languages is not likely to be efficient, because that typically results in repeatedly evaluating the logarithm of j, multiplying by b, and exponentiating the result. When lot sizes are large—tactical missiles, munitions, and radios may be built in lots of several thousand units—this takes considerable time. Naive evaluation in spreadsheets also has that problem, as well as the awkwardness of filling thousands of cells when lot sizes are in the thousands.

It seems that more thoughtful evaluation algorithms can help a good deal. Often, one can benefit from available analytic and numerical results to make accurate and efficient algorithms to evaluate functions that have been studied. Sums of negative powers of integers do appear in the mathematical literature. For example, the Riemann zeta function $\zeta(s)$ is defined by

$$\zeta(s) \equiv \sum_{1}^{\infty} j^{-s} \tag{48}$$

for s with real parts larger than one.

Cost analysts would be interested in a sort of "incomplete zeta function" of the form

$$\zeta(s, N) \equiv \sum_{1}^{N} j^{-s} \tag{49}$$

since

$$\sum_{L}^{U} j^{b} = \zeta(-b, U) - \zeta(-b, L - 1) \tag{50}$$

That function does not appear to be discussed in the literature, however.

It seems appropriate to define the special functions that we need, and then study their properties to develop efficient evaluation algorithms. I believe it is appropriate to recognize Harold Asher's contributions by naming the functions for him. Accordingly, I'll define the three-argument Asher function $A(L, U, b)$ as:

$$A(L,U,b) \equiv \sum_{L}^{U} j^b \qquad (51)$$

and the two-argument Asher function **A(U, b)**

$$A(U,b) \equiv \sum_{1}^{U} j^b \qquad (52)$$

These functions are of direct interest to cost analysts, and they may be studied to make efficient evaluation algorithms.

The two functions are, obviously, related in a simple way:

$$A(L,U,b) = A(U,b) - A(L-1,b) \qquad (53)$$

For the rest of the book, we'll use Asher functions to facilitate work with Crawford cost-progress models.

We may use a well-known result in numerical analysis to provide a sequence of corrections, with error bounds, for Asher's approximation (46) of **A(L, U, b)**. The corrected values can be used in algorithms that generate numerical values of **A(L, U, b)** to any required precision, often much more quickly than evaluating the sum directly.

The well-known result is the second Euler-Maclaurin summation formula.[13] Applied to our case, it shows that

$$A(L,U,b) = \frac{(U+0.5)^{1+b} - (L-0.5)^{1+b}}{1+b} -$$

$$\sum_{i=1}^{m} \frac{1 - 2^{1-2i}}{(2i)!} B_{2i} \left[f^{(2i-1)}_{(U+0.5)} - f^{(2i-1)}_{(L-0.5)} \right] + E_m \qquad (54)$$

---

[13] Hildebrand, F. B., *Introduction to Numerical Analysis,* Second Edition, McGraw-Hill, New York, 1974, p. 20.

In (54), B_{2i} is the $2i^{th}$ Bernoulli number,[14] $f(x) \equiv x^b$, and $f_{(x)}^{(k)}$ denotes the kth derivative of f. The Bernoulli numbers are rational numbers; numerators and denominators for the first 10 values of the B_{2i} are shown in Table 1.

i	N_i	D_i	i	N_i	D_i
1	1	6	6	−691	2,730
2	−1	30	7	7	6
3	1	42	8	−3,617	510
4	−1	30	9	43,867	798
5	10	66	10	−174,611	330

Table 1. Numerators and Denominators for Bernoulli Numbers: $B_{2i} = N_i/D_i$

Equation (54) can be interpreted as Asher's approximation (46) (the first term on the right side) with correction terms (the summation on the right side) and an error term, E_m. All the derivatives of $f(x)$ that appear have a constant sign in the intervals of interest, and as Hildebrand points out,[15] this is sufficient to guarantee that the error E_m is numerically smaller than the first neglected term of the sum. This gives a computable error bound on the approximation to $A(L, U, b)$ provided by taking any finite number of terms in the sum.

To illustrate the nature of the approximations to $A(L, U, b)$ provided by taking finite values of m, here is the one for $m = 1$:

---

[14]Abramowitz, M. and I. Stegun, *Handbook of Mathematical Functions*, Dover, New York, 1965, p. 804 et seq.

[15]Hildebrand, F. B., l. c. ante.

$$A(L,U,b) \approx \frac{(U+0.5)^{1+b} - (L-0.5)^{1+b}}{1+b} -$$
$$\frac{b}{24}\left[(U+0.5)^{b-1} - (L-0.5)^{b-1}\right] \tag{55}$$

The error in approximation (55) will not exceed

$$\frac{7}{5760} b(b-1)(b-2)\left[(U+0.5)^{b-3} - (L-0.5)^{b-3}\right] \tag{56}$$

Because the sum in (54) is not a convergent series, (54) alone cannot be used to provide arbitrary accuracy. Like Asher's approximation, (54) with any given number of terms becomes less accurate for smaller **L** and algebraically smaller **b** (i.e., for steeper slopes). With any fixed **m**, (54) can be shown to be an asymptotic approximation to **A(L, U, b)** in the parameter **L**.

A few terms of (54) do, however, often give useful results for fairly small values of **L**. Numerical experiments show, for example, that (54) is capable of providing eight-figure accuracy for **L** as low as 5, for **b** as small as –0.98 (i.e., a cost-progress curve slope of slightly more than 50 percent) with only 5 correction terms.

Asher's approximation alone does not give eight-figure accuracy until **L** is rather large, on the order of a few hundred, for **b** = –0.3 (roughly 80 percent slope.) Therefore, the correction terms speed accurate calculation considerably.

The correction terms in (54) look rather complicated. One may evaluate them, however, with simple recursion relations, using only arithmetic operations. No powers need be computed once Asher's approximation has been evaluated.

Of course, approximations generated by taking finite **m** in (54) should be used only when they give the desired accuracy in less computing time than would be required to sum the defining series. Numerical experiments indicate that the series should be used instead of (54) whenever $U - L$ is five or less.

The Appendix gives a Visual Basic function that evaluates $A(L, U, b)$ to eight-figure accuracy. One may copy this function into a Microsoft Excel® workbook module, to have $A(L, U, b)$ as readily available in Excel spreadsheets as any other library function such as $\sin(x)$.

SLOPES OF 50 PERCENT OR STEEPER AROUSE SUSPICION

Since $b = \ln(S)/\ln(2)$, if S is steeper than 50 percent, then the corresponding b is smaller than -1. Now, $\sum_{1}^{\infty} j^{b}$ converges if b is smaller than -1. Consequently, on a cost-progress curve with a slope of less than 50 percent, indefinitely many units could be produced for finite cost. Of course, the zero unit-cost limit of any Wright or Crawford curve with slope less than 1 is itself suspect, but slopes as steep as 50 percent are really questionable.

WRIGHT AND CRAWFORD MODELS ARE INDISTINGUISHABLE AT LARGE QUANTITIES

Equation (41) shows that, in the Wright model, the cost $C(Q)$ of the Qth production unit is given by

$$C(Q) = A_1\left[Q^{b+1} - (Q-1)^{b+1}\right] \tag{57}$$

How does this expression for the cost of unit Q compare with the Crawford model cost of unit Q, $T_1 Q^b$, for large values of Q?

By the binomial series, we have (for $Q > 1$):

$$(Q - 1)^{b+1} = Q^{b+1} \left(1 - \frac{1}{Q} \right)^{1+b} = Q^{1+b} \left[1 - \frac{1+b}{Q} + O(Q^{-2}) \right] \quad \textbf{(58)}$$

Substituting this result into (57) and simplifying shows that in the Wright model, for large values of Q,

$$C(Q) = A_1 (1+b) Q^b \left[1 + O(Q^{-1}) \right] \approx A_1 (1+b) Q^b \quad \textbf{(59)}$$

Thus, for large Q, the unit costs of a Wright model cost-progress curve with parameters A_1 and b become indistin–guishable from those of a Crawford model curve with the same value of b and theoretical first-unit cost $\hat{T}_1$ given by

$$\hat{T}_1 = A_1 (1+b) \quad \textbf{(60)}$$

ESTIMATING LEARNING CURVE PARAMETERS FROM LOT COST DATA

In this section, we use the tools developed in the mathematical preliminaries to solve the tasks mentioned at the start of the chapter.

WRIGHT AND CRAWFORD LOT COSTS FROM COST OF INITIAL LOT AND SLOPE

When estimating production costs at a program's early stages, before even the costs of producing articles in development phases are known, analysts use cost-estimating relationships (CERs). As described in Chapter 4, CERs generate estimates of production costs from performance parameters characterizing the new item. Typically, CERs for production costs give production costs for an initial lot, e.g., the first 10, the first 100, or the first 1,000 units.

Given the CER's output, the analyst's job is to find the lot-by-lot costs of the planned production sequence (the buy plan) for the new item. In addition to the value of an initial lot provided by the CER, an analyst generally has an estimate of a cost-progress curve slope appropriate to the planned production of the new item.

We'll have the required sequence of lot costs if we can generate the cost of an arbitrary lot, from initial quantity **L** to final quantity **U**, given the cost of the initial lot that began with item number L_0 and ended with item U_0. Let y_0 denote the given cost of that initial lot. With the Wright model, we have

$$A_0\left[U_0^{1+b} - (L_0 - 1)^{1+b}\right] = y_0 \tag{61}$$

where **b** is the exponent corresponding to the chosen slope. Then

$$A_0 = \frac{y_0}{U_0^{1+b} - (L_0 - 1)^{1+b}} \tag{62}$$

and the required cost **y** of the lot comprising items **L** through **U** is

$$y = y_0 \frac{U^{1+b} - (L - 1)^{1+b}}{U_0^{1+b} - (L_0 - 1)^{1+b}} \tag{63}$$

If we work with the Crawford (unit) model instead of the Wright model, instead of the notation of (61) we would have

$$T_0 A(L_0, U_0, b) = y_0 \qquad (64)$$

and (63) would be replaced by

$$y = y_0 \frac{A(L, U, b)}{A(L_0, U_0, b)} \qquad (65)$$

ESTIMATING COST-PROGRESS CURVE PARAMETERS FROM LOT COST DATA

The other tasks described in the introduction to this chapter all require estimating parameters of cost-progress curves from lot cost data. We now turn to that task. We deal with Crawford (unit model) curves first.

The general idea is a natural and obvious one: given costs of a few lots, find the parameters of the Crawford curve that best fits the observed costs, in some sense of "best fit." It would be comforting if we knew that such best-fit parameters always existed.

A NONEXISTENCE PROBLEM

Unfortunately, that is not true. Usually, this nonexistence does not cause trouble, and straightforward estimating methods do yield a solution. Nevertheless, the nonexistence can be a problem: iterative schemes may fail to converge or different analyses of the same data can give different results. It is a good idea to be aware of the possibility.

It is easy enough to see the reason for the nonexistence problem. It is rooted in the fact that there are monotone nonincreasing sequences of unit costs $\{c_1, c_2, \ldots\}$, such that the minimization problem

$$\min_{T_0, b}\left[\sum_{1}^{N}\left(c_j - T_0 j^b\right)^2\right] \qquad (66)$$

has no solution. For example, consider the cost sequence $\{1, 0, 0, 0, \ldots\}$. Taking $T_0 = 1$, one can make the penalty function of (66) closer and closer to zero by taking algebraically smaller values of the exponent b. But there is no "best" value of b: the penalty function decreases to zero from above as b approaches $-\infty$.

Specialists in approximation theory have studied problems like (66), which turn out to be fairly subtle.[16] Since the subtleties seem not often to bother cost analysts, we won't go into them here. Those interested can enter the literature with the reference of Footnote 16.

BEST LEAST-SQUARES FIT

Analytically, one can find best-fit Crawford parameters, when they exist, quite straightforwardly. For example, seeking the Crawford parameters that minimize the sum of the squares of the differences between observed lot costs and the corresponding Crawford lot costs leads to

$$\min_{T_0, b}\left\{\sum_{1}^{N}\left[y_i - T_0\, A(L_i, U_i, b)\right]^2\right\} \qquad (67)$$

---

[16] See, for example, Cheney, W., *Introduction to Approximation Theory*, Second Edition, Chelsea, New York, 1991.

The solution of the unconstrained minimization problem (67) will be the solution of the pair of simultaneous equations

$$\sum_1^N \left[y_i - T_0 A(L_i U_i, b)\right] A(L_i, U_i, b) = 0 \tag{68}$$

and

$$\sum_1^N \left[y_i - T_0 A(L_i U_i, b)\right] \frac{\partial A(L_i, U_i, b)}{\partial b} = 0 \tag{69}$$

when those equations have a unique solution. It is, in principle, relatively easy to find approximate numerical values for the T_0 and b of that solution, when it exists. Equation (68) leads to

$$T_0 = \frac{\displaystyle\sum_1^N y_i A(L_i, U_i, b)}{\displaystyle\sum_1^N \left[A(L_i, U_i, b)\right]^2} \tag{70}$$

Substituting (70) into (69) gives a single equation for **b**:

$$\sum_{i=1}^N \left[y_i - \frac{\displaystyle\sum_{j=1}^N y_i A(L_j, U_j, b)}{\displaystyle\sum_{k=1}^N \left[A(L_k, U_k, b)\right]^2} A(L_i U_i, b) \right] \frac{\partial A(L_i, U_i, b)}{\partial b} = 0 \tag{71}$$

Similar considerations to the ones that led to efficient evaluation of **A(L, U, b)** in the mathematical preliminaries section of this chapter also lead to efficient evaluation of $\frac{\partial A(L, U, b)}{\partial b}$. With this, the solution of (71), when it exists, may in principle be approximated with guaranteed accuracy by bisection. Also, when there is no solution to (67), the left side of (71) will have one sign for all **b**. This gives a useful way to spot such cases.

Since analysts generally have available reasonably effective routines for generating numerical approximations directly to the solution of (67), the present discussion is helpful mainly for understanding the nature of the minimization problem. I will not give the code for numerical evaluation of $\dfrac{\partial A(L,U,b)}{\partial b}$.

All the above "in principle" qualifiers are included because there can be difficulties with finding numerical approximations. Some approximations are discussed in the section "A Note on Sensitivity and Errors," below.

CHOOSING THE PARAMETER-ESTIMATING METHOD IN VIEW OF A STATISTICAL ERROR MODEL

In the preceding section, we confidently used the y_i, the actual values of the lot costs, as though we knew them precisely. This is hardly ever true: what we really know are "noisy" values $\tilde{y}_i$ of the lot costs. The $\tilde{y}_i$ depart from the values of a Crawford curve for two reasons: the Crawford model is not likely to be perfectly correct; there are almost certain to be various observation errors (defective cost accounting, late or inaccurate reports, and the like). Differing assumptions about the "errors" in the $\tilde{y}_i$ (i.e., about the way in which the $\tilde{y}_i$ depart from the y_i) make differing parameter-estimation methods appropriate.

One common assumption about those departures is that

$$\tilde{y}_i = y_i + \varepsilon_i \tag{72}$$

$$\tilde{y} = y + \varepsilon$$

where ε_i is the total error of the ith observation. This is known as the additive error model. Another error model, the multiplicative error model, is given by

$$\tilde{y}_i = y_i(1+\varepsilon_i) \tag{73}$$

The least-squares minimization of the preceding section is a particularly appropriate method of estimating the cost-progress curve parameters, when the additive error model applies. If the additive errors ε_i are assumed to be independent, identically distributed zero-mean normal random variables, then the least-squares estimating method gives maximum-likelihood estimates.[17] That is, the least-squares values of T_0 and $\mathbf{b}$ are the ones that maximize the probability of observing the set $\{\tilde{y}_1, \tilde{y}_2, \dots, \tilde{y}_N\}$ of noisy values that actually was observed.

If, however, one assumes that the errors are multiplicative, and further, that they are independent, identically distributed zero-mean normal random variables, then a maximum-likelihood estimator for T_0 and $\mathbf{b}$ is given approximately by[18]

---

[17] P. G. Hoel, *Introduction to Mathematical Statistics*, Fifth Edition, Wiley, New York, 1984, p. 234 et seq.

[18] The probability of observing the sequence $\{\tilde{y}_1, \tilde{y}_2, \dots, \tilde{y}_M\}$ is

$$\frac{\exp\left[-\dfrac{1}{2\sigma^2}\sum_1^M \left(\dfrac{\tilde{y}_i}{T_0 A(L_i, U_i, b)} - 1\right)^2\right]}{\left[\sqrt{2\pi}\sigma T_0\right]^M \prod_1^M A(L_j, U_j, b)}$$

where σ is the common standard deviation of the ε_i The exponential in the numerator of this expression is much more sensitive to variations in T_0 and $\mathbf{b}$ than is the denominator. The numerator is maximized by the solution of (74). Maximizing

$$\min_{T_0,\, b}\left\{\sum_{1}^{N}\left[\frac{\tilde{y}_i}{T_0 A(L_i, U_i, b)} - 1\right]^2\right\} \tag{74}$$

Which error model is appropriate? In general, when values of the observations range over several orders of magnitude, multiplicative errors are likely to be more appropriate. When, rather, the observations' values differ by less than a factor of two or three, additive errors are probably a better assumption.

It is a good idea to check, after estimation, that the chosen error model was consistent with the data. If one is using the additive model, one considers the differences between the observed lot costs and the lot costs generated by the fitted T_0 and b, and asks whether or not it is reasonable to regard them as draws from a set of independent, zero-mean normal random variables with common variance. Using the multiplicative model, one considers the quantities $\frac{\tilde{y}_i}{T_0 A(L_i, U_i, b)} - 1$, and asks the same question.

Statisticians refer to errors for which the variance is not constant as "heteroscedastic." There is substantial literature on quantitative tests for heteroscedasticity.[19] The classical tests often require separating the cases into two or more classes and so they may not be particularly helpful when sample sizes are as small as they often are in cost analysis. It is usually a good idea to look at the error plots, even if one does apply quantitative tests.

---

the entire expression, using an estimate for σ obtained from the residuals of the fitted curve, typically leads only to minor changes from the solution of (74).

[19]Judge, George G., et al, *The Theory and Practice of Econometrics*, Chapter 4, "Heteroscedasticity," Wiley, New York, 1980.

EXAMPLES

Table 2 gives observed costs for eight production lots of a tactical missile. The ratio of the largest to the smallest observed lot cost is about three, which suggests that additive error is appropriate. Accordingly, solving the minimization problem (67) leads to estimated values of T_0 and b of 2.233 and –0.3497, respectively. That exponent corresponds to a slope of 78.47 percent.

Lot Start	Lot End	Lot Cost	
1	218	102.765	*minimum*
219	1,158	212.158	
1,159	3,200	321.819	
3,201	5,900	333.720	*maximum*
5,901	7,591	212.558	
7,592	10,011	227.238	
10,012	11,668	157.912	
11,669	14,436	171.339	

Table 2. Lot Start and End Values and Lot Costs for Tactical Missile

It is a good idea to see how well the model fits the data. Since the data are lot costs, we should see how well our Crawford model of lot costs fits them. Figure 5 shows this:

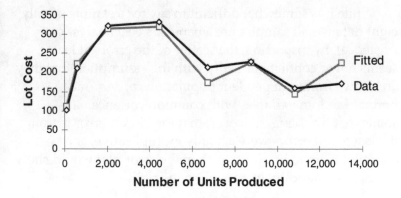

Figure 5. Comparison of Data and Modeled Lot Costs

The fit seems reasonable, although it is clearly worse at the fifth and eighth points than at the other points.

To check that the additive error model was appropriate, we examine the errors of the modeled lot costs, shown in Figure 6.

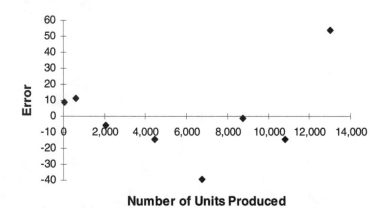

Figure 6. Errors in Modeled Lot Costs

While it is somewhat difficult to say for a sample of only eight data (small samples are a bane of a cost analyst's existence), by inspection, the scatter of the errors at least seems not to conflict markedly with the assumption that they are draws from independent populations of zero-mean normal random variables with common variance. It is somewhat troubling, however, that the largest error is from the last lot: if errors were actually multiplicative, and we assumed them to be additive, then the error plot would show errors systematically increasing to the right.

It is also somewhat difficult to apply standard tests for heteroscedasticity when the sample is so small. A version of Glesjer's test[20] fails to reject homoscedasticity at 90 percent confidence, but would reject it with 85 percent confidence. On balance, I'd be inclined to accept the additive model.

Confidence in that choice is strengthened by the fact that, when one repeats the analysis with the multiplicative model, the fifth and eighth points again are potential outliers (see Figure 7 and Figure 8).

---

[20]Judge, George G., et al, l. c. ante, p. 145.

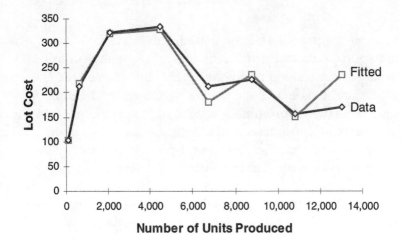

**Figure 7. Comparison of Data and Modeled Lot Costs
(Multiplicative Error Model)**

And the corresponding errors are:

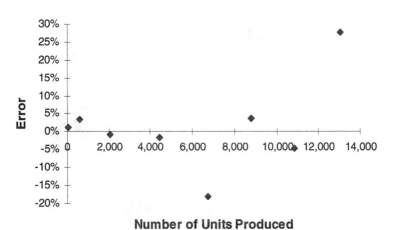

**Figure 8. Errors in Modeled Lot Costs
(Multiplicative Error Model)**

The comparisons between model and data that I've shown are appropriate and helpful for analyzing goodness of fit, because they show directly the agreement between the chosen model and the data. Lot costs are not, however, helpful indicators of cost progress when lot sizes vary. Unit costs are of course the appropriate indicators. Cost analysts often compare data and models in a unit-cost view showing lot average costs, plotted at the plot point determined by the slope of the fitted cost-progress curve, with logarithmic scales on both axes. Figure 9 shows this comparison for the present case.

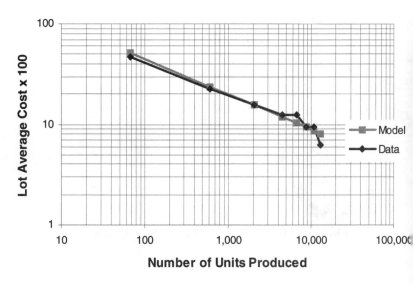

Figure 9. Traditional Comparison of Data and Model

A CLASSIC COST-PROGRESS CURVE FITTING METHOD USING LINEAR REGRESSION

Cost analysts have long used a method of inferring "best-fit" Crawford curves that involves linear regression. If one assumes the multiplicative error model (73), then the lot-average costs $\tilde{z}_i$, defined by

$$\tilde{z}_i \equiv \frac{\tilde{y}_i}{L_i - U_i + 1} \tag{75}$$

also have multiplicative error. Specifically, if the "correct" values of the lot costs y_i are those of a Crawford cost-progress curve, then it follows from the definition (45) of the plot point $\bar{x}_{L,U}(b)$ that

$$\tilde{z}_i = T_1 \bar{x}_i^b(b)(1 + \varepsilon_i) \tag{76}$$

where $\bar{x}_i(b)$ is a shortened notation for $\bar{x}_{L_i, U_i}(b)$.

Equation (76) implies that

$$\ln(\tilde{z}_i) = \ln T_1 + b \ln[\bar{x}_i(b)] + \ln(1 + \varepsilon_i) \tag{77}$$

If $|\varepsilon_i| \ll 1$, then $\ln(1 + \varepsilon_i) \approx \varepsilon_i$. With the usual assumptions that the ε_i are independent, identically distributed normal random variables with zero mean and common standard deviation σ, it follows that in this "small relative error" approximation the quantities $\ln(\tilde{z}_i)$ are independent, identically distributed normal random variables, whose probability densities are given by

$$\ln(\tilde{z}_i) \sim N\{\ln(T_1) + b \ln[\bar{x}_i(b)], \sigma\} \tag{78}$$

It then follows that the likelihood of the observed sequence of noisy values $\ln(\tilde{z}_1), \ln(\tilde{z}_2), \ldots \ln(\tilde{z}_N)$ is maximized by the T_1 and b that solve

$$\min_{T_1, b} \sum_{1}^{N} \left\{ \ln(\tilde{z}_i) - \ln(T_1) - b \ln\left[\bar{x}_i(b)\right] \right\}^2 \qquad (79)$$

Now, problem (79) looks almost like linear regression of the $\ln(\tilde{z}_i)$ on the $\ln\left[\bar{x}_i(b)\right]$. It would be that linear regression if the $\bar{x}_i$ did not depend on b. It turns out that, starting with an initial guess b_0 for b, regressing the $\ln(\tilde{z}_i)$ on the $\ln\left[\bar{x}_i(b_0)\right]$, identifying $\ln(T_1)$ with the constant term of the regression, taking the regression coefficient of the $\ln\left[\bar{x}_i(b_0)\right]$ as a new estimate for b, and repeating the process—often generates a rapidly converging sequence of estimates for T_1 and b. (Indeed, relying on rapid convergence, some less-careful practitioners do not bother with more than one iteration.)

While this procedure may appear to make the wealth of information that is known about linear regression available to the estimation of cost-progress curve parameters, the dependence of the $\bar{x}_i$ on b is a complication whose consequences seem not easily seen. Today's practitioners almost always have more straightforward means of estimating cost-progress curve parameters.

RATE ADJUSTMENTS

Table 3 shows production cost data for another missile program:

Lot Start	Lot End	Lot Cost
1	80	56.6
81	316	81.2
317	599	76.4
600	1,234	128.6
1,235	2,918	255.1
2,919	5,069	278.6
5,070	7,573	274.1
7,574	9,929	243.9
9,930	12,129	207.2
12,130	13,967	168.7
13,968	17,448	288.3
17,449	18,662	113.6
18,663	19,508	81.5

**Table 3. Lot Start and End Values and Lot Costs for
Another Missile Program**

Recalling that the economic justification for cost progress (Chapter 2) is based on manufacturing at the constant lot quantity for which a plant was designed, we note that the lot quantities of Table 3 actually vary over nearly an order of magnitude from the lowest to highest, and by more than ±50 percent from the mean value (Figure 10).

Clearly, the constant-rate assumption is not met in this case. Production rate effects can indeed be important, and in this section, we develop means to account for them.

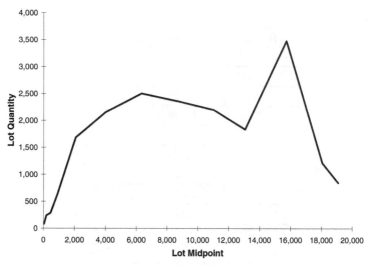

Figure 10. Production Rates (Lot Quantities) vs. Cumulative Production Quantity

There are two production rate effects: economies or diseconomies of scale, which appear when production rates change together with plant size; and the effects of production at other than a facility's designed rate, which appear when production rates change more rapidly than plant size. A single, consistent perspective enables us to treat both effects together. As we do so, we will recover two classical rate-adjustment methods, and our approach will let us see when it is appropriate to apply each of them.

A production function describes the relation between the inputs and outputs of a firm or of a segment of the economy.[21] A convenient example production function, considering two factors of production **K** and **L**, has the form

---

[21] Watson, Donald S., *Price Theory and Its Uses*, Chapter 9, "The Theory of Production," Third Edition, Houghton-Mifflin, Boston, 1972.

$$R = R_0 \left(\frac{K}{K_0} \right)^\alpha \left(\frac{L}{L_0} \right)^\beta \qquad (80)$$

where **R** is the amount of product generated by efficient use of amounts **K** and **L** of the two factors, and **R₀**, **K₀**, **L₀**, α, and β are constants. (Since **R₀**, **K₀**, and **L₀** can be collapsed into a single constant, the production function of (80) has just three adjustable constants.) We regard the production factors **K** and **L** as capital (investment in plant) and labor, respectively.

If the prices of **K** and **L** are **p_K** and **p_L**, respectively, then an efficient facility for production at rate **R₁** should have inputs **K** and **L** that solve

$$\min_{K,\,L} (p_K K + p_L L), \text{ subject to } R_0 \left(\frac{K}{K_0} \right)^\alpha \left(\frac{L}{L_0} \right)^\beta = R_1 \qquad (81)$$

Straightforward (but somewhat lengthy) use of standard methods (e.g., an application of Lagrange multipliers) gives the solution of (81):

$$\frac{L}{L_0} = \left[\frac{R_1}{R_0} \left(\frac{\beta}{\alpha} \frac{p_K}{p_L} \frac{K_0}{L_0} \right)^\alpha \right]^{\frac{1}{\alpha+\beta}} \qquad (82)$$

and

$$K = \frac{\alpha}{\beta} \frac{p_L}{p_K} L \qquad (83)$$

Equations (82) and (83) lead, after considerable manipulation, to an expression for the lot average cost **z** as

$$z = \frac{1}{R_0} p_L L_0 \left(\frac{\alpha}{\beta} + 1 \right) \left(\frac{\beta}{\alpha} \frac{p_K}{p_L} \frac{K_0}{L_0} \right)^{\frac{\alpha}{\alpha+\beta}} \left(\frac{R_1}{R_0} \right)^{\frac{1-(\alpha+\beta)}{\alpha+\beta}} \qquad (84)$$

Equation (84) recovers the well-known result that there are economies of scale if $\alpha + \beta > 1$, diseconomies of scale if $\alpha + \beta < 1$, and no scale effects if $\alpha + \beta = 1$.

We can get more. Design changes for improved producibility will change the production function. If these, together with the results of investments in production technology, have the effect of making

$$\frac{1}{R_0} p_L L_0 \left(\frac{\alpha}{\beta}+1\right)\left(\frac{\beta}{\alpha}\frac{p_K}{p_L}\frac{K_0}{L_0}\right)^{\frac{\alpha}{\alpha+\beta}} = T_1 Q^b \qquad (85)$$

while keeping $\alpha + \beta$ constant,[22] then lot average costs would have the form

$$z = T_1 Q^b \left(\frac{R_1}{R_0}\right)^c \qquad (86)$$

This suggests one of the classical production rate adjustments to cost-progress curves,

$$C(Q) = T_1 Q^b \left(\frac{R}{R_0}\right)^c \qquad (87)$$

As the arguments that led us to it show, this adjustment is plausible when the factors of production can change with rate, to keep the facility operating at its designed rate. It certainly is reasonable to assume that these efficient adjustments are made when we are considering plants that have not yet been built.

---

[22]Making a detailed treatment of this glib "if" would be an interesting challenge. One not-implausible way for this to happen would be for L_0 to decrease like a power of Q, while the other parameters remained constant.

If, however, we are dealing with operations in an existing plant, this may not be the case. Our parameter K represents capital, which amounts to things such as factory floor space, specialized machinery, and tooling. These things certainly can be changed, but if the production rate changes abruptly, it may prove impossible to change K in the short term. In contrast, the work force, represented by our parameter L, usually can be changed more quickly than capital assets.

To see what may happen with abrupt changes in rate, that force operating a plant at other than its design rate, let's suppose that K is fixed at the efficient value for rate R_1, while L is changed to cause production at rate R_2. If K is fixed at a value K_1, then to produce at rate R_2 we must have

$$R_0 \left(\frac{K_1}{K_0} \right)^{\alpha} \left(\frac{L}{L_0} \right)^{\beta} = R_2 \tag{88}$$

Solving (88) for L and evaluating the lot average cost gives, after some manipulation,

$$z = \frac{p_K K_1}{R_2} + p_L L_0 \left[\frac{1}{R_0} \left(\frac{K_0}{K_1} \right)^{\alpha} \right]^{\frac{1}{\beta}} R_2^{\frac{1}{\beta} - 1} \tag{89}$$

If investments in producibility and production technology cause R_0 to increase like a power of total production quantity Q, and if output varies roughly linearly with L, so that $\beta \approx 1$, then the lot average cost z will be the sum of a term inversely proportional to the current rate R_2, and a term independent of R_2 that varies as a negative power of Q. This suggests modeling the cost of the Qth item as

$$C(Q) = \frac{F}{R} + T_1 Q^b \tag{90}$$

Equation (90) is another widely used model for production rate effects: the cost of a lot is equal to a constant fixed cost F, plus costs that descend a Crawford cost-progress curve.

It is simple enough in principle to find the parameters T_1, b, and c of the power-law rate-effect model, or the parameters F, T_1, and b of the fixed-cost rate-effect model. The art of the matter comes in deciding which model is appropriate (and, perhaps, in coping with the problems identified in the section "A Note on Sensitivity and Errors").

For examples of the use of rate adjustments, let us work on the following problem: suppose that we are given the data of Table 3 only for the first nine lots and are required to use them to forecast the costs of the remaining lots. In this exercise, we will do what is *not* good practice of cost analysis: we will tinker with different mathematical models of cost progress until we get reasonably good fits to data. In good practice, one uses detailed information about the program in question to make such critical choices as selecting the power-law or fixed-cost model of rate adjustment. Only in this way can the fairly crude available tools be used with some confidence to treat the complex acquisition situations that cost analysts face continually.

Figure 11 shows the fit of a simple Crawford cost-progress curve to the first nine lots and the resulting forecast for the costs of the remaining lots.

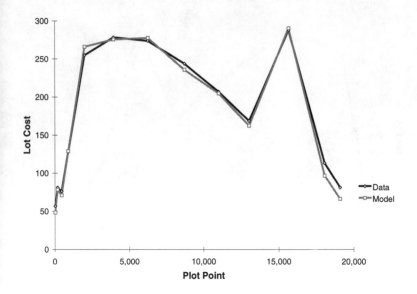

Figure 11. Fit and Forecast, Crawford Model

While the simple Crawford model does quite well with the isolated, large lot, it misses the other three forecast lots fairly significantly.

Figure 12 shows the result of fitting a Crawford curve with power-law rate adjustment to the first nine lots' data from Table 3. Certainly, the rate adjustment has improved the forecast. The power-law model is appropriate, however, only if the plant was reconfigured for each lot to make the actual rate the optimal rate.

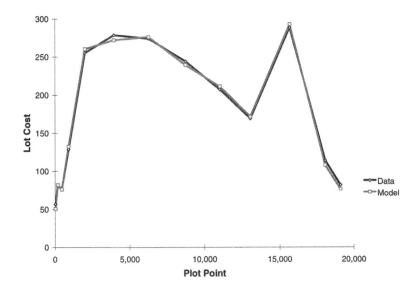

Figure 12. Comparison of Fit and Forecast, Power-Law Rate-Effect Model

Perhaps that was not done. Let's see if a fixed-cost rate adjustment does better. To do so, we must deal with the fact that the fixed-cost model almost certainly is not appropriate for the early lots, when the plant is "ramping up" to full-rate production.

One way to do this is simply to start fitting to data for the first full-rate lot. This wastes data, however. One can avoid that by using the fixed-cost model in a composite cost-progress curve, in which the ramp-up lots are fit to a power-law rate-adjusted model and subsequent lots to a fixed-cost model, with a continuity condition imposed to make the two models consistent with a single production facility.

Figure 10 suggests that the sixth lot is the first full-rate lot. Accordingly, we make that lot the one for which the power-law model and the fixed-cost model in our composite curve give the same cost.

Specifically, our composite curve will be

$$y_i = T_1 A(L_i, U_i, b)\left(\frac{V_i}{2000}\right)^c \tag{91}$$

for $i = 1, 2, \ldots, 6$, and

$$y_i = \hat{T}_1 A(L_i, U_i, \hat{b}) + F \tag{92}$$

for $i = 6, 7, \ldots, 12$. Continuity at lot 6 requires that

$$T_1 A(L_6, U_6, b)\left(\frac{V_6}{2000}\right)^c = \hat{T}_1 A(L_6, U_6, \hat{b}) + F \tag{93}$$

which we meet by choosing F to satisfy

$$F = T_1 A(L_6, U_6, b)\left(\frac{V_6}{2000}\right)^c - \hat{T}_1 A(L_6, U_6, \hat{b}) \tag{94}$$

Figure 13 shows the fit and forecast of the resulting composite curve.

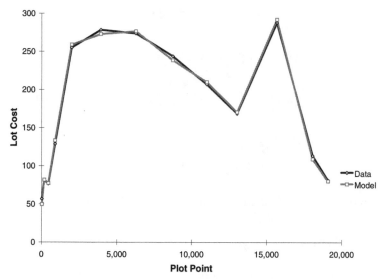

Figure 13. Fit and Forecast of Composite Rate-Adjusted Curve

The composite curve clearly does the best overall forecast in this case. However, I must emphasize that, in good practice, one's choices of models should be guided by information about programs, not by apparent goodness of fits.

As an *awful warning* on that point, notice the rather good fit of a composite cost-progress curve in the example of Figure 14.

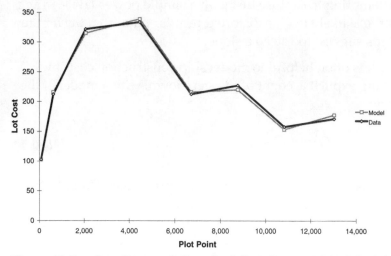

Figure 14. Lot Cost Data and Crawford Cost-Progress Model with Composite Rate Adjustment

The "join" of the composite curve is at the fourth lot. While the model fits the data reasonably well, forecasts for substantially larger total quantities would probably be too low: the slope of the constant fixed-cost model is 42 percent! What is actually going on in this case is that production was moved to a new facility starting with the fifth lot. An appropriate learning curve model would start afresh at unit 1 for data from the new plant. When this is done, much more reasonable slopes are found. The resulting models are, of course, much more likely to give acceptable forecasts.

COST-PROGRESS CURVES FOR CAPITAL SHIPS

Capital ship projects typically impute many costs to the leadship of a class. Consequently, there is usually a marked "step down" from the leadship to the first followship. Attempting to capture this with a simple power-law learning curve is likely to give distorted results: data from the first few ships suggest too steep a slope.

It is often helpful to model ship construction costs by taking explicit account of the step down, with a model of the form

$$\text{Cost of } j^{\text{th}} \text{ ship of class} = \begin{cases} T_1, & j = 1 \\ \alpha T_1 j^b, & j > 1 \end{cases} \quad \textbf{(95)}$$

Acquisition of capital ships also proceeds in "flights," which are groups of ships in a class. A class of, say, 50 ships might have 5 or 10 flights, typically consisting of ships built in a given set of years, whose members have similar specific modifications. Leadships of flights also have extra costs imputed to them and an adjustment similar to (95) may be appropriate for leadships of flights, too. If this is done, the model becomes

$$\text{Cost of } j^{\text{th}} \text{ ship of class} = \begin{cases} T_1, & j = 1 \\ \alpha T_1 j^b, & j > 1 \text{ and not lead ship of flight} \\ \alpha\beta T_1 j^b, & j > 1 \text{ and lead ship of flight} \end{cases} \quad \textbf{(96)}$$

A NOTE ON SENSITIVITY AND ERRORS

In this chapter and others, I spoke of the solutions of certain minimization problems as though we could evaluate them precisely, so long as the problems had solutions. In practice, unfortunately, that is not always so easy to do.

Even when a problem has a unique solution, generating good numerical approximations to the solution may be difficult or even impossible. For example, suppose we wished to infer the parameters of a power-law rate-adjusted Crawford cost-progress curve for the data of Table 4. Suppose also, for simplicity, that we have determined that the additive error model is appropriate despite the large variation in lot costs.

Lot Size	Lot Cost
1	500.0
3	906.3
8	1,488.9
22	2,530.9
61	4,331.8
168	7,374.1
463	12,566.9

Table 4. Example Lot Sizes and Costs

The data of Table 4 are contrived: to the accuracy of the six-decimal numbers shown, the lot costs are equal to the lot costs of a power-law rate-adjusted Crawford curve with first-unit cost 500, quantity slope 80 percent, and rate slope 90 percent. Thus, the problem of minimizing the sum of the squares of the differences between the lot costs of the data and the lot costs of a power-law rate-adjusted Crawford curve has a solution—and it is possible to show that the solution is unique.

Nevertheless, working with these data, a widely available and reasonably reliable optimizing routine converges to significantly different values of T_1, quantity slope, and rate slope, depending on where it is started. For example, one test led to $T_1 = 500.2$, quantity slope = 81.5, and rate slope = 88.3, while another resulted in $T_1 = 498.6$, quantity slope = 72.02, and rate slope = 100 (rate slopes were constrained not to exceed 100 percent). Such differences in slopes will, obviously, give drastic differences in costs of following lots, as cumulative quantities increase.

Moreover, if instead of the precise lot costs of Table 4, lot costs that scatter a few percentages from them are input, the routine converges—after many iterations—to wildly different results. One set of trials produced quantity slopes ranging from 82.99 percent to 40.83 percent!

Clearly, something is badly amiss. What is it? It is this: not only are the data of Table 4 contrived to be exact lot costs of a certain cost-progress model, the lot sizes are contrived to confound the problem of minimizing the sum of the squares of the errors. At an unconstrained minimum, the condition that the partial derivatives of the sum of the squares of the errors with respect to T_1, b, and c each equal zero leads to three equations, which have the forms

$$\sum \left[\tilde{y}_i - T_1 A_i(b) R_i^c \right] A_i(b) R_i^c = 0 \qquad (97)$$

$$\sum \left[\tilde{y}_i - T_1 A_i(b) R_i^c \right] A_i'(b) R_i^c = 0 \qquad (98)$$

$$\sum \left[\tilde{y}_i - T_1 A_i(b) R_i^c \right] A_i(b) \ln(R_i) R_i^c = 0 \qquad (99)$$

In each of these equations, the sum ranges over all observations, and $A_i(b) \equiv A(L_i, U_i, b)$.

In general, when there are stationary points, as there are at unconstrained minima, the three equations serve to determine values of the three parameters T_1, b, and c.

The data of Table 4 are maliciously contrived, however, so that

$$A_i(b)\ln(R_i) \approx A'i(b) \qquad \textbf{(100)}$$

The approximation is good to at least three significant figures for all points except the first, where it is good to about 6 percent. Now, if the approximation of (100) were an equality, Equations (97), (98), and (99) would amount to only two different equations in T_1, b, and c. Two conditions do not, in general, determine three things uniquely, and so there would be, typically, a family of solutions to Equations (97), (98), and (99), rather than just one.

When rates and quantities are closely related, as they are for the lot sizes of Table 4, while technically there may still be a unique solution to the minimization problem, values of the sum of the squared errors will have about the same, relatively small value for many different values of rate slope and quantity slope. Small changes in the data, for example, in the lot cost data, can cause wide swings in the solution of Equations (97), (98), and (99).

Viewed another way, when the rates R_i are determined by the $A_i(b)$, we do not have independent variation of rates and quantities. It is not surprising that, in such a case, we cannot get information about both quantity slope and rate slope.

This kind of difficulty arises in linear regression, when some members of the set of independent variables at which observations are made are linear functions of the others. In that case, the problem is known as "multicollinearity." The term is also often used to describe more general cases—such as the one we are considering—when one independent variable for a nonlinear minimization problem is a function of others.

I give a fairly detailed treatment of one problem of this kind in Chapter 5, in the section "The 'Small-Time Problem' of

Rayleigh Analysis." The general problem for cost analysis leads to the interesting and related topics of error propagation and the statistics of estimates. Treating those topics would require another book. For now, I'll stop with recommending the discussion of multicollinearity found in Chapter 12 of *The Theory and Practice of Econometrics*, by Judge, et al.[23]

SUMMARY

In this chapter, we discussed several ways in which cost analysts use cost-progress curves. We considered the use of statistical models to develop maximum likelihood estimates of the parameters of cost-progress models, and we saw how classical economic ideas give a consistent perspective on two widely used rate-adjustment models.

Analysts generally find the resulting methods useful, when some actual cost data are available for the item under study. Many times, however, estimates must be made without such data. The following chapter treats methods for such cases.

---

[23] Judge, George C., et al, *The Theory and Practice of Econometrics*, Chapter 12, Wiley: New York, 1980.

CHAPTER 4

COST-ESTIMATING RELATIONSHIPS

In the previous chapter, we dealt with cost-progress curves at some length. From this, we have useful ideas about how to estimate parameters of a cost-progress curve model like $C_j = T_1 j^b$, given cost and quantity data for a few lots, and we can use such cost-progress models to estimate costs of subsequent lots. Now let's think about estimating costs of producing a given set of lots for a new item on which we have no production cost data.

In particular, how might we estimate the theoretical first-unit cost T_1 for such an item? Often, it is possible to model observed values of T_1 for a class of items with a function whose arguments are variables related to the performance of the items or to specific features of their designs. That is, we can make models of the form

$$T_1 = f(x_1, x_2, \ldots, x_n) \tag{101}$$

Such an expression is called a cost-estimating relationship, or CER. Often, CERs give not the theoretical first-unit cost, but some quantity related to it, such as the total cost of the first few units.

Our discussion of CERs has two purposes: to help you be an intelligent *user* of CERs and to help you be an effective *maker* of CERs when you need to "roll your own."

USING CERS

Let's begin the "using" part by looking at some examples. Often it is helpful to make CERs, not for an entire complex item like a radar or an airplane, but, rather, to decompose the complex machine into functional components and develop individual CERs for these components. The following pages show examples of such decompositions, and some of the individual CERs, for production costs of radars and missiles. They are taken from several reports from Management Consulting and Research, Incorporated (MCR).[24]

MCR's Radar Production Cost Model consists of CERs for each radar subsystem. Here are their results for two of those components. For the radar Structure/Feed (S/F) system manufacturing cost, MCR developed the following CER:

$$\text{Cost}_{S/F} = 5.48 \times \text{Aperture}^{1.05} \times (10.859 \times \text{End\_Feed}) \times \quad \textbf{(102)}$$

$$\text{PCFH}(\text{Qty}_{cum}, \text{Qty}_{lot})$$

where

Aperture	= Antenna aperture in square feet;
End_Feed	= 1 if the antenna is a slotted array fed from one end, 0 if not;
PCFH()	= Production cost function for hardware;
Qty_{cum}	= Cumulative quantity of radar production units for current lot;
Qty_{lot}	= Total lot quantity of radar production units.

This CER produced the following results:

---

[24] Witt, Sandra L., et al, *Electro-Optical, Missile, Radar and Avionics System Cost Research*: Volume 1, *Radar Production Cost Model*, and Volume 3, *Missile Production Cost Model*, Management Consulting and Research, Inc., Report TR-8740-2, May 1988.

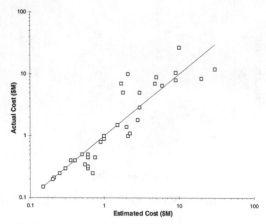

Figure 15. Production Cost Model—Radar Structure/Feed

In a similar manner, MCR developed a CER for the Phase Shifter (PS) component (the first equation models PSs using ferrites and the second models PSs using diodes):

$$\text{Cost}_{\text{PS}} = \begin{cases} 49.3 \times \text{PS}^{0.848} \times \left(\dfrac{\text{Pwr}}{\text{MAX}(1,\text{PS})} \right)^{0.599} \times \text{PCFH}(\text{Qty}_{\text{cum}}, \text{Qty}_{\text{lot}}) \\[2em] 1.31 \times \text{PS}^{0.848} \times \left(\dfrac{\text{Pwr}}{\text{MAX}(1,\text{PS})} \right)^{0.225} \times \text{B} \times \text{PCFH}(\text{Qty}_{\text{cum}}, \text{Qty}_{\text{lot}}) \end{cases}$$

where

PS $\equiv$ Number of phase shifters employed in the antenna.

Pwr $\equiv$ Average power produced by the transmitter (in kilowatts).

B $\equiv$ The number of bits of phase shift.

PCFH(), Qtycum, and Qtylot are as defined above.

This CER produced the following results:

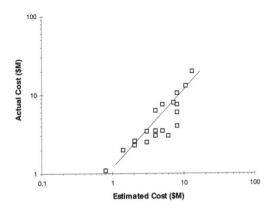

Figure 16. Production Cost Model—Radar Phase Shifters

EXPLANATORY VARIABLES

A CER's arguments are called its explanatory variables. Some of the sample CERs use what we may call "performance" explanatory variables—for example, power for a transmitter and aperture for an antenna. Others use explanatory variables not directly related either to performance or to the value of the item. An example of such a "nonperformance" explanatory variable is weight for a missile control system.

Generally, CERs whose explanatory variables relate to performance or to the value of an item are more likely to be helpful than others. This is particularly so when, as is often the case for defense projects, it is necessary to estimate costs of systems whose properties are not close to those of the systems on which the CER was calibrated.

Weight is a particularly tricky explanatory variable. It is often used—and it may be used successfully. Weight is, however, almost always a proxy for other features that actually drive cost. When using CERs in which weight is an explanatory variable, it is a good idea to think carefully about what the real determinants of cost are likely to be and to consider how useful weight is likely to be as a proxy for them. Also, it is important to think carefully about how consistent the weight proxy is likely to be among the cases on which a weight-based CER was calibrated and the item you are estimating. Changes in manufacturing and design may radically change the weight-value relations. For example, replacing lumped-component designs with integrated circuits makes such a change for electronics, as does the use of modular zone construction methods for shipbuilding.

Neglecting performance and considering weight alone certainly can give distorted impressions. Hemm points out that costs of fielded spacecraft consistently increase with weight.[25] This seems paradoxical, since spacecraft designers work in a cost-weight trade space in which reducing weight for a spacecraft with given performance generally increases cost, as shown in Figure 17.

Hemm argues convincingly that the explanation of the paradox is that heavier spacecraft typically have greater performance than lighter ones. This also is illustrated by Figure 17. Neglecting this feature of the data might lead the unwary—or the unscrupulous—to suggest that, on the basis of data, lighter spacecraft are cheaper than heavier ones, so the way to make spacecraft of a given performance capability cheaper is to make them lighter. As the cost-weight curves of Figure 17 show, just the opposite is typically the case.

---

[25]Hemm, R., *A Down-to-Earth Approach to Space Launch*, Logistics Management Institute internal paper, 1996.

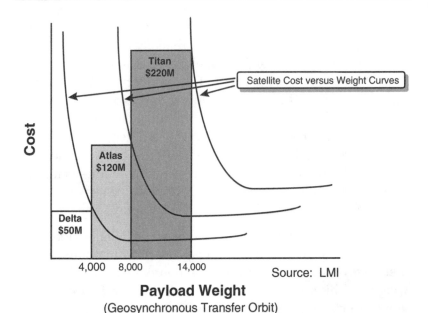

Payload Weight
(Geosynchronous Transfer Orbit)

Figure 17. Satellite Trade Spaces and Realized Costs

A more subtle distortion may be about to enter spacecraft data, to the confusion of those who neglect performance and consider only weight. New launch vehicles are intended to reduce sharply the cost to launch a given weight of spacecraft into a given orbit. So far, the limited payloads and high cost per pound in orbit of launch rockets have justified substantial expense to make spacecraft light. The overall optimum-cost system is usually one in which the spacecraft design point lies well to the left of the minimum on the cost-weight curve. If, however, launch costs per pound come down significantly, the optimal spacecraft for a given performance may be further to the right on the cost-weight curve, closer to the minimum cost point. Then, newer systems of given performance will weigh more—and cost less—than older ones.

These points are not to say that you must not use weight as an explanatory variable. Indeed, we will do just that in some of the following examples. Rather, the idea is to think carefully about how you do it.

GOODNESS OF FIT

Typically, the maker of a CER will give a chart comparing the predictions of the CER with the data on which it was calibrated. Like weight as an explanatory variable, goodness of fit can be useful, but it requires thought. Certainly it is good to see that a CER fits its data reasonably well. Nevertheless, it is better to have a tolerably good fit and sensible explanatory variables and functional forms, than to have excellent fit with implausible functional forms and arbitrary explanatory variables. Variables and functional forms introduced solely for tradition or mathematical convenience are particularly suspicious.

If someone offers a CER with the functional form

$$\text{Cost} = C_0 (\text{weight})^p (\text{length})^q e^{\alpha(t-t_0)} \qquad \textbf{(103)}$$

she has the duty to explain why those explanatory variables—and that functional form—make physical and economic sense.

Here is an example of how thoughtless mathematical "finesse" and devotion to good fit can lead one astray. To make the actual behavior of the thing to be modeled utterly clear, we consider modeling the position of a sphere falling in a near vacuum.

For physical reasons, to a very good approximation the position $x(t)$ of the sphere at time t actually is given by $x(t) = \frac{g}{2} t^2$. Consequently, a thoughtful worker would try to predict the sphere's position, given observations of its positions at a few initial times, by fitting a function $\hat{x}(t) = ct^2$ to the data. Ignoring the physics and thinking only of good fit, one might try to make predictions with a higher-order polynomial, say, a cubic polynomial of the form $\bar{x}(t) = c_0 + c_1 t + c_2 t^2 + c_3 t^3$.

Figure 18 shows a set of five noisy position data, with fitted square-law and cubic models. The fitting method was least squares. The cubic model clearly fits these initial data better than the square law.

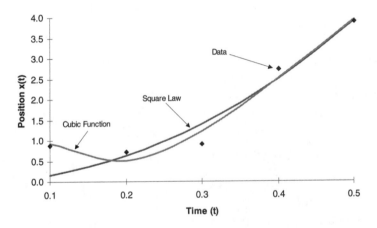

Figure 18. Five Initial Data and Two Models

Now, let's see what happens when we use the two models to predict further observations. Figure 19 shows subsequent position data, corrupted by the same noise process that produced the first four data, with predicted values generated from the square-law and from the cubic model.

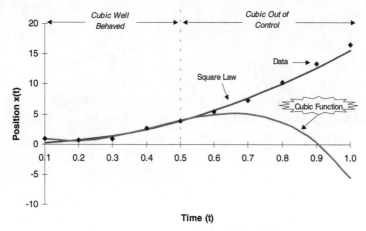

Figure 19. Further Data and the Two Models

The cubic function fits well only over the interval on which it was calibrated. As a predictor outside that interval, it's a disaster. This bad behavior, thoroughly characteristic of interpolating polynomials, shows how important it is to consider physical and economic facts in choosing explanatory variables and functional forms for CERs.

BUILDING CERS

If you cannot find a ready-made CER suitable for the task at hand, but you can find appropriate data, it may be helpful to develop your own CER. The rest of this chapter sets out a general guiding idea for doing that and illustrates it with an example.

The guiding idea has two parts. First, choose explanatory variables (independent variables) that characterize *performance* of the things whose costs are to be estimated. Second, use basic engineering, physics, or statistics to *relate* the performance variables to cost (dependent variable). This approach improves the chances for the resulting CER to give useful results over a wide range of performance characteristics.

For the reasons stated above, CERs made this way are likely to give much better results than those made with the all-too-common approach of choosing explanatory variables for traditional (e.g., weight) and functional forms for mathematical convenience (e.g., power law with adjustable exponent). Below is an example of *performance-based CERs*.

EXAMPLE—SHIP STRUCTURAL AND PROPULSION COSTS

As an example, let's consider estimating the cost of a ship's structure and propulsion. Even at an early stage of a ship project, we are likely to know such performance parameters as displacement and speed because these relate directly to the ship's missions. Accordingly, let's work with these explanatory variables and use basic engineering models—rather than an arbitrarily chosen mathematical form—to develop our CER.

SHIPS' DISPLACEMENTS

Ships' displacements are commonly described in two ways:

- Full-load displacement, D_{fl}, is (roughly) the ship's weight when loaded to planned capacity, including fuel, mission equipment, stores, furniture, and the like.

- Lightship displacement, D_{ls}, is (roughly) the ship's weight when empty of stores, fuel, and furnishings.

How might we expect hull construction costs to vary with displacement? Would the variation have one form for D_{fl} and another for D_{ls}? We address those questions with engineering models.

For high-level analyses, marine architects use a simple model of a ship's hull, the simple beam model. As shown in Figure 20, this model characterizes the entire ship's structure as a single beam. This model is adequate to capture the effects of longitudinal stress, moments, and shear profiles.[26]

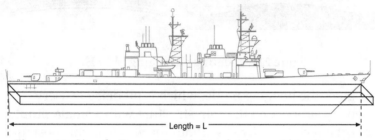

Length = L

Figure 20. Simple Beam Model Overlaid on a Ship Structure

The two load conditions shown (in Figures 20 and 21) are the most stressing cases. In both, the ship experiences waves whose wavelength is about equal to the ship's length.

In Figure 21, wave crests have raised water levels at bow and stern.

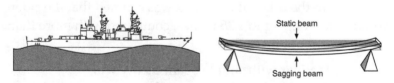

Static beam

Sagging beam

Figure 21. Modeling a Sagging Ship Hull

---

[26] Gran, S., "A Course in Ocean Engineering," *Developments in Marine Technology*, Number 8, Elsevier Science Publishers, Netherlands, 1992, p. 348.

Simplistically and conservatively, this is like supporting the structure with simple supports at bow and stern. This gives the sagging mode.

In Figure 22, a crest is amidships, with troughs at bow and stern.

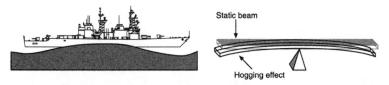

Figure 22. Modeling a Hogging Ship Hull

This gives the hogging mode, which is modeled conservatively by supporting the ship structure with a single simple support amidships. Even without the waves in this position, hogging often naturally occurs, since the midship section has more buoyancy than the bow and stern sections. As a point of interest, a recent issue of *National Geographic* magazine noted that hogging of the *USS Constitution* (known as "Old Ironsides") decreased sharply after the addition of diagonal riders. These riders were in the original plans for the *Constitution*, but they were missing from the actual finished structure. In the original papers, it was claimed that the riders would limit hogging to 1.25 inches, compared with more than 13 inches without them.[27]

Those familiar with simple beam theory will see immediately that in both hogging and sagging modes, the

---

[27]Marden, Luis, "Restoring Old Ironsides," *National Geographic*, Volume 191, June 1997, pp. 49–51.

section of the beam with maximum bending moment—and thus, maximum stress—is at the center of the ship.[28]

The maximum bending moment is $D_{fl} \dfrac{L}{8}$, where **L** is the ship's length. Equating this to the moment of the distribution of stresses in the beam's cross section gives

$$D_{fl} \frac{L}{8} = \frac{\sigma_{mx}}{\beta} \lambda^2 dA \qquad (104)$$

where σ_{mx} is the maximum stress allowed in the beam, **d** is the depth of the ship's basic structure, and **A** is a representative cross-sectional area. The nondimensional parameters β and λ relate **d** to the maximum distance from the beam's neutral axis to a point in the cross section and to the radius of gyration of the cross section, respectively.

Now, the weight of the structure **Ws** is related to the cross-sectional area **A** by

$$W_s = g\rho_s AL \qquad (105)$$

where ρ_s is a representative density of the structure material. Using (105) to express **A** in terms of **Ws**, substituting the result in (104), solving for **Ws** and arranging the terms gives the following expression for **Ws**:

$$Ws = \frac{g}{8} D_{fl} \left(\frac{L^2}{d} \right) \left(\frac{\beta}{\lambda^2} \right) \left(\frac{\rho_s}{\sigma_{mx}} \right) \qquad (106)$$

The grouping of terms in Equation (106) shows that, in the approximation of the beam model, the weight of a ship's

---

[28]Those who'd like a refresher may consult any of several excellent references, for example, Hahne, H. V., *Handbook of Engineering Mechanics*, Chapter 35, "Bending of Beams," W. Flugge, Editor, McGraw-Hill, New York, 1962.

structure is proportional to the full-load displacement multiplied by a factor characteristic of the ship's overall geometry (the factor L^2/d), a factor characteristic of the geometry of a representative cross-section (the factor β/λ^2), and a factor characteristic of the material of which the structure is made (the factor ρ_S/σ_{mx}).

Instead of a maximum stress σ_{ms}, a maximum strain design limit often is appropriate. In this case, the maximum displacement of the structure is limited to a specified fraction ε_{mx} of the ship's length. If the ship is designed to a maximum strain constraint, then the relation between structure weight and full-load displacement takes the form

$$W_S = \frac{5g}{384} D_{fl} \left(\frac{L^3}{d^2} \right) \left(\frac{1}{\lambda^2} \right) \left(\frac{\rho_S}{E_S} \right) \left(\frac{1}{\varepsilon_0} \right) \qquad (107)$$

Here again, W_S is proportional to D_{fl}, through factors characteristic of the ship's overall geometry, geometry of the cross-sectional area, and hull material. The symbol E_S denotes the Young's modulus of the hull material; it is a measure of the material's inherent stiffness. The factor $\dfrac{1}{\varepsilon_0}$ in (107) reflects the fact that, for given geometry and material, a stiffer hull structure (one that deforms less under load) will be heavier.

RELATION OF PROPULSION COST TO FULL-LOAD DISPLACEMENT AND SPEED

Now, let's develop a model of the relations among propulsion cost, full-load displacement, and speed. When a ship travels at Froude number F that is not small compared with 1, and is not close to 0.4, then the power P required to drive her at speed V is given approximately by

$$P = C_T \frac{1}{2} \rho_w V^3 A_S \qquad (108)$$

where ρ_w is the water's density, A_S is the cross-sectional area of the submerged part of the hull, and C_T is a constant. We can readily relate P to V, full-load displacement D_{fl}, and the ship's length L, by using the fact that the weight of water that the ship displaces must equal her weight:

$$g\rho_w A_S L = D_{fl} \qquad (109)$$

Solving (109) for A_S, inserting the result in (108), and simplifying gives

$$P = \frac{C_T}{2g}\left(V^3\right)\left(\frac{1}{L}\right)D_{fl} \qquad (110)$$

Now, let's assume that the cost of the ship's structure is proportional to its weight, and that the cost of propulsion is proportional to power. Both these assumptions seem plausible, and they can be checked against data. Very likely, special construction techniques will change the cost-weight relation for structures, and different kinds of power plants (for example, steam, gas turbine, diesel) may have different cost-power relations. If we know what these differing relations are, we can introduce them into our model. For now, however, we simply take

$$C = p_1 W_S + p_2 P \qquad (111)$$

Inserting W_S from (106) and P from (110) gives our basic model for cost as a function of full-load displacement and speed:

$$C = \left[\frac{g}{8}\left(\frac{\rho_S}{\sigma_{mx}} \right)\left(\frac{\beta}{\lambda^2} \right)\left(\frac{L}{d}L \right)p_1 + \frac{C_T}{2g}\left(V^3 \right)\left(\frac{1}{L} \right)p_2 \right]D_{fl} \quad \textbf{(112)}$$

Next, we develop an expression for cost in terms of lightship displacement D_{ls}. If we approximate D_{ls} as the sum of W_S and the weight of propulsion W_P, we may take

$$D_{ls} = W_S + \frac{P}{r_{PW}} \quad \textbf{(113)}$$

where the power-to-weight ration r_{pw} is a characteristic of the kind of propulsion plant used. Again using (106) and (110) to express W_S and P, respectively, in terms of D_{fl}, gives an expression for D_{ls} in terms of D_{fl}:

$$D_{ls} = \left[\frac{g}{8}\left(\frac{\rho_S}{\sigma_{mx}} \right)\left(\frac{\beta}{\lambda^2} \right)\left(\frac{L}{d}L \right) + \frac{C_T}{2gr_{pw}}\left(V^3 \right)\left(\frac{1}{L} \right) \right]D_{fl} \quad \textbf{(114)}$$

Solving (114) for D_{fl}, substituting the result in (112), and then simplifying gives our basic expression for cost as a function of lightship displacement:

$$C = \frac{p_1 + Rr_{pw}p_2}{1+R}D_{LS} \quad \textbf{(115)}$$

where the nondimensional parameter R is given by

$$R = \frac{4C_T V^3 d}{g\left(\frac{g\rho_S L}{\sigma_{mx}} \right)\left(\frac{\beta}{\lambda^2} \right)\frac{L}{d}Lr_{pw}} \quad \textbf{(116)}$$

In calibrating either of the CERs (112) or (115), we may choose, depending on the data at hand, how many of the potentially observable parameters such as L, d, β, σ_{mx}, and so on, to include. We may decide that all the ships used for calibration have essentially the same value of hull cross-section parameter $\left(\dfrac{\beta}{\lambda^2}\right)$, as well as essentially the same

material property parameter $\left(\dfrac{\rho_S}{\sigma_{mx}}\right)$. In that case, we would

calibrate (112) in the form:

$$C = \left(c_1 \frac{L^2}{d} + c_2 \frac{V^3}{L}\right) D_{fl} \qquad (117)$$

where c_1 and c_2 are adjustable constants, and where **L**, **d**, **V**, and $\mathbf{D_{fl}}$ are observed. If, however, we chose to consider other parameters in (112) and had data for them, we would include these other parameters in the calibration.

While we made the CERs (112) and (115) to illustrate the idea of using physical and engineering models in developing CERs, they give reasonably good results. (Of course, developing a CER that one wished actually to use would probably require considerably more attention to the specifics of the problem at hand. Figure 23 (at the end of this chapter) shows the fit of (112), calibrated under the assumption that hull cross-sections and materials were essentially the same for all ships, to several ship classes.

To include several ships from the same class, we took the cost determined by (112) to be the leadship cost and estimated slope and leadship-followship stepdown with the other parameters (see Chapter 3 for a discussion of the ship cost progress curve that we used). Specifically, we modeled the cost of the $\mathbf{N^{th}}$ ship of a class as

$$C = \begin{cases} C^*, & N = 1 \\ \alpha C^* N^b, & N > 1 \end{cases} \qquad (118)$$

where

$$C^* \equiv \frac{c_1 + c_2 \dfrac{v^3 d}{L^3}}{1 + c_3 \dfrac{v^3 d}{L^3}} D_{ls} \tag{119}$$

and estimated c_1, c_2, c_3, α, and **b**.

In Figure 23, the axis label "Ship Sequence" means the sequence of ships of a given class in a given shipyard. That is, the ship with Ship Sequence 1 is the first ship of the class in the yard. Ship Sequence 2 is the second ship of the class in the yard, and so on.

SUMMARY

In this chapter, we considered the use and development of cost-estimating relationships. For development, we saw how using explanatory variables that characterize system performance and taking functional forms from physical and engineering models, leads to effective results. We saw, from an example, that such physically consistent CERs are likely to make better forecasts than those made with explanatory variables chosen just for tradition, and functional forms chosen just for tradition or for mathematical convenience (even when they do not fit the data as well).

In the next chapter, we turn to estimating costs of development programs.

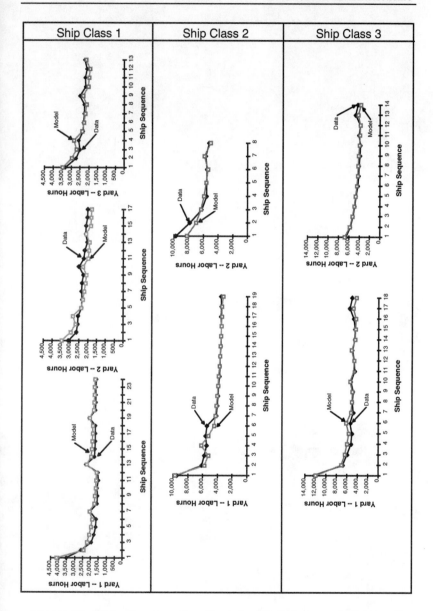

Figure 23. Ship Construction Costs by Hull Type and Shipyard

CHAPTER 5

THE RAYLEIGH MODEL OF DEVELOPMENT PROGRAMS' COST PROFILES

The cost-progress curves discussed in Chapter 3 have many uses in analyzing and estimating costs of *production* programs. Among these are

- Predicting "cost-to-go," given data on the costs and quantities of initial lots

- Generating time-phased expenditure profiles, given an estimate for total cost.

It would be convenient to have a model for *development* projects that would help one to do the same tasks.

There is in fact such a model. Known as the "Rayleigh" or "Norden-Rayleigh" model, it has been considerably developed over the past decade or so.

Norden[29] seems to have been the first to suggest that well-managed development programs absorb resources proportional to the Rayleigh distribution. This idea may be expressed

$$v(t) = d\left(1 - e^{-at^2}\right) \qquad \textbf{(120)}$$

where **v(t)** denotes the total value of expenditures on the program at time **t**; **a** and **d** are adjustable parameters. In a

---

[29]Norden, V. P., "Useful Tools for Project Management," of *Management of Production*, M. K. Stan, Editor, Penguin, Baltimore, 1970, pp. 71–107.

later paper, Paar showed how complex problem-solving exercises in which, at the beginning, each problem solved enables work to begin on other problems, would lead to a resource-absorption pattern like that of (120).[30] Paar developed a resource-absorption pattern different from that of (120), but with a similar shape.

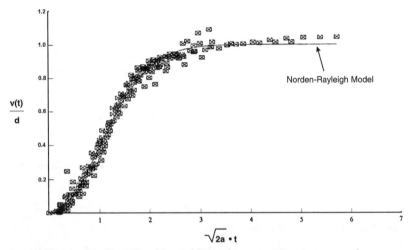

Figure 24. Cost Profiles of Development Programs and Norden-Rayleigh Model

Several studies have shown that the Norden-Rayleigh model is a good one for the development parts of major defense acquisition programs.[31,32] Figure 24, taken from the paper by

[30]Paar, F. N., "An Alternative to the Rayleigh Curve Model for Software Development," *IEEE Transactions on Software Engineering*, May 1980, pp. 291–296.

[31]Watkins, H., "An Application of Rayleigh Curve Theory to Contract Cost Estimation and Control," Master's Thesis, U.S. Navy Naval Postgraduate School, 1982, directed by Professor Dan C. Boger.

[32]Abernethy, T., "An Application of the Rayleigh Distribution to Contract Cost Data," Master's Thesis, U.S. Navy Naval Postgraduate School, 1984, directed by Professor Dan C. Boger.

Lee, Hogue, and Hoffman,[33] shows how well the model collapses data from several tens of defense programs onto a single curve.

In view of the results shown in Figure 24, we may take the Rayleigh distribution model as having as good an empirical justification as the power-law learning curve models and then explore its uses.

DETERMINING AN OUTLAY PROFILE FROM AN ESTIMATE OF TOTAL DEVELOPMENT COST

The application to "spreading" an estimate for the total costs of a development program is almost immediate. There is one point to resolve: since the Rayleigh distribution does not reach its maximum value of 1.0 at finite time, we must find a way to relate the total cost of a program to a finite completion time.[34] One way to do that is to associate the program's completion time with the time at which $v(t)$ reaches some fixed fraction of the limiting value d. Somewhat arbitrarily, I and others have chosen this fixed fraction to be 97 percent. This conventional completion point is the rightmost highlighted point in Figure 25.

---

[33]Lee, D. A., M. R. Hogue, and D. C. Hoffman, "Time Histories of Expenditures for Defense Acquisition Programs in the Development Phase-Norden-Rayleigh and Other Models," Presented at the 1993 Annual Meeting of the International Society of Parametric Analysis.

[34]This feature is not as unrealistic as one might think: development programs for major defense acquisitions actually often do continue for several years, at relatively small and decreasing annual expenditures, before their formal conclusions.

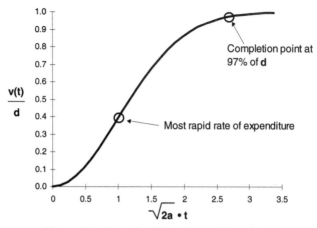

Figure 25. Standard Rayleigh Distribution

In this convention, the program's total cost is 0.97**d**. The convention's completion time **t$_f$** is related to the time-scale parameter **a** by

$$t_f = \sqrt{\frac{-\ln(0.03)}{a}} \approx \frac{1.8726}{\sqrt{a}} \qquad (121)$$

Alternatively, the time-scale parameter **a** may be expressed in terms of **t$_f$** by

$$a = \frac{-\ln(0.03)}{t_f^2} \approx \frac{3.5066}{t_f^2} \qquad (122)$$

While it is not needed for the spreading exercise, the point of most rapid rate of expenditure on the program **t$_p$**, shown as the leftmost highlighted point in Figure 25, will be useful in the following analyses. The parameter **t$_p$** is related to the time scale parameter **a** by

$$t_p = \frac{1}{\sqrt{2a}} \qquad (123)$$

The time-scale parameter **a** may be determined from t_p by

$$a = \frac{1}{2t_p^2} \qquad (124)$$

There is a rule of thumb that a development program will expend 60 percent of its total cost in the first half of its total time. With our conventional t_f and the Rayleigh model, a program would spend 60.2 percent of its total cost at time $t_f/2$.

Now we can solve the spreading problem. Given an estimate for a development program's total cost **D**, measured in constant dollars of some fixed year, and an estimate for completion time t_f, one may develop a spread of the program's constant-dollar expenditures by determining a Rayleigh parameter **d** from

$$d = D / 0.97 \qquad (125)$$

and a Rayleigh time-scale parameter **a** from (122). Then, the expenditure $v_{1,2}$ from time t_1 to time t_2 is given by

$$v_{1,2} = v(t_2) - v(t_1) = d\left(e^{-at_1^2} - e^{-at_2^2}\right) \qquad (126)$$

One may determine annual amounts of total obligational authority required to fund a development program from the constant-dollar expenditure profiles generated from the Rayleigh model.[35]

---

[35] Lee, D. A., M. A. Gallagher, and M. R. Hogue, "Determining a Budget Profile from an R&D Cost Estimate," *Journal of Cost Analysis*, Fall 1997, pp. 29 et seq.

FORECASTING DEVELOPMENT COSTS FROM OBSERVED COSTS OF INITIAL PERIODS

To use the Rayleigh model for forecasting, one must infer values of the Rayleigh time scale parameter **a**, and the limiting cost parameter **d**, from data on the expenditures for a few initial lots. This is analogous to using cost-progress curves for forecasting the costs of subsequent lots, given the costs of a few initial lots.

It is not at all difficult to infer maximum-likelihood estimates of the Rayleigh parameters. For example, let us take the multiplicative error model

$$\tilde{y}_i = d\, z_i(a)(1 + \varepsilon_i) \tag{127}$$

where $\tilde{y}_i$ denotes the noisy, observed values of the development program's costs in the ith period, which begins at time t_{i-1} and ends at time t_i, and where

$$z_i(a) \equiv e^{-at_{i-1}^2} - e^{-at_i^2} \tag{128}$$

Then, with the usual assumptions that the ε_i are independent, identically distributed zero-mean normal random variables with common standard deviation σ, the quantities $\tilde{y}_i / z_i(a) - d$ will be independent normal random variables with mean 0 and common variance $d\sigma$. It follows that the likelihood of observing the sequence $\left\{ \tilde{y}_1, \tilde{y}_2, ..., \tilde{y}_N \right\}$ is maximized approximately (see Footnote 18) by the values of **a** and **d** that solve

$$\min_{a,d} \sum_1^N \left(\frac{\tilde{y}_i}{z_i(a)} - d \right)^2 \qquad (129)$$

When it exists, the solution of problem (129) is readily determined by making the penalty function stationary with respect to **a** and **d**. This leads to

$$d = \frac{1}{N} \sum_1^N \frac{\tilde{y}_i}{z_i(a)} \qquad (130)$$

which determines **d** as a function of **a**, and to

$$\sum_1^N \left[\frac{\tilde{y}_i}{z_i(a)} - \frac{1}{N} \sum_{j=1}^N \frac{\tilde{y}_j}{z_j(a)} \right] \frac{\tilde{y}_i}{z_i^2(a)} z_i'(a) = 0 \qquad (131)$$

Numerical approximations to the solution of (131), when it exists, can be generated with guaranteed error bounds by bisection.

No doubt you will have gathered from all those "when it exists" statements that—just as was the case for Crawford cost-progress curves—there are cases in which the solution does not exist. Unfortunately, the nonexistence is more troublesome for Rayleigh models. We will see the troubles—and an approach to dealing with them—in the following section.

AN EXAMPLE

Table 5 shows an example of the per-period expenditures on a development program and the time, measured in days from program start, at the ends of the periods.

Days from Start	Cost Increment (constant-dollar units)
161	23.57
253	25.51
344	35.33
434	50.57
526	69.55
618	81.24
709	77.95
800	73.19
892	73.30
984	55.86

**Table 5. Incremental Expenditures on Example
Development Program**

The cost increments are the $\tilde{y}_i$, and the "days from start" are the t_i. The dimensions of the $\tilde{y}_i$ are, in effect, constant dollars. (I won't give a precise definition of "constant-dollar units," nor calendar dates, to avoid identifying the program.)

The data of Table 5 describe a case for which the minimization problem (129) does have a unique solution. The solution is $a = 1.065 \times 10^{-6}$, $d = 858.5$. The data are compared with the model in Figure 26:

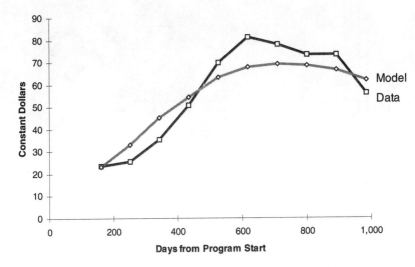

Figure 26. Comparison of Data and Model

Figure 27 shows a plot of the errors $\dfrac{\tilde{y}_i}{z_i(a)} - d$. The error plot (Figure 27) at least does not show flagrant heteroscedasticity, and we may consider our a and d values reasonable inferences from the data.

The data of Table 5 are for a real program, so we can compare the forecast completion time and final cost with what actually happened.

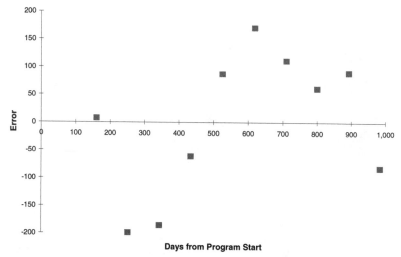

Days from Program Start

Figure 27. Error Plot

Figure 28 compares the actual cumulative costs with those predicted by the model. The predicted total cost is within about 6 percent of the actual total cost. Comparison of the actual and forecast completion times is complicated by the fact that for this program, as for many others, small amounts were charged to the development program over a considerable time after the great bulk of development money was spent. The t_f from (121) is 1,814 days. The real program took 1,895 days to spend 97 percent of the last total cost recorded. Perhaps that is the fairest comparison of predicted and actual completion times. With this comparison, the predicted completion time is roughly 4 percent less than the actual completion time.

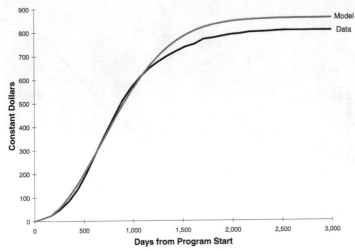

**Figure 28. Comparison of Actual Cost and Cost
Predicted by Model**

THE "SMALL-TIME PROBLEM" OF RAYLEIGH ANALYSIS

The Rayleigh model would, it seems, have succeeded fairly well if applied to the example program when 10 period costs were available. What if it had been applied at a much earlier time, say, when only 5 period costs were at hand? The model still fits the data about as well as before, as indicated by Figure 29.

The results, however, are bad: they forecast a completion time of 1,293 days and a final cost of 438 constant-dollar units. What has gone wrong?

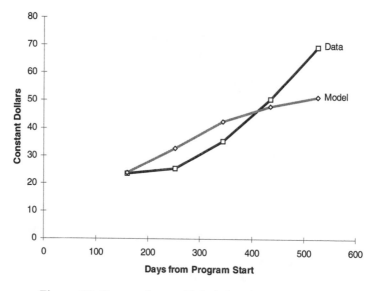

Figure 29. Comparison of Model and Data—Fewer Points Available

The difficulty lies in the nature of the Rayleigh model itself, specifically in the functions $dz_i(a)$ that represent the increments of cost in the Rayleigh model. When the value of t_i is so small that $at_i \ll 1$ for all i, then

$$dz_i(a) \approx ad(t_i^2 - t_{i-1}^2) = 2ad\,\overline{t}_i\,\Delta t_i \qquad (132)$$

where

$$\overline{t}_i \equiv 0.5(t_i + t_{i-1}); \quad \Delta t_i \equiv (t_i - t_{i-1}) \qquad (133)$$

As we see from (132), when the t_i are small in this sense, the values of $dz_i(a)$ depend only on the product ad. Thus, Rayleigh curves with very different time scales and total costs have incremental cost profiles that are quite close together, for sufficiently small times. The situation is illustrated in Figure 30.

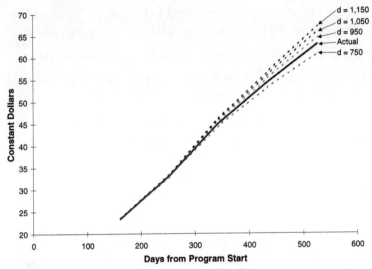

Figure 30. Significantly Different Rayleigh Curves Imply Neighboring Expenditure Profiles for Small-Time Values

The time values shown in Figure 30 are the same as those of the first five data in Table 5. The curve labeled "Actual" has the same **a** and **d** parameters as the best-fit Rayleigh curve shown in Figure 28. The other curves have **d** parameters ranging from 750 to 1,150 constant-dollar units, and times t_f ranging from 1,688 to 2,091 days; yet, their expenditure profiles are within the range –3.5 percent (+6.5 percent of those of the "Actual" curve), over the times considered.

The fact that widely differing Rayleigh curves have cost profiles very close together for "short" times, makes any attempt to infer both **a** and **d** from real (i.e., noisy) short-time data futile.

The nature of the $z_i(a)$ also underlies a nonexistence fact: the problem (129) has no solution if the $\tilde{y}_i$ correspond to funding rates that are proportional to t_i. For, by (132), in that case one can make the distances between the $dz_i(a)$ and the $\tilde{y}_i$ arbitrarily small by taking **a** sufficiently small and **d** sufficiently large, while keeping the product **ad** equal to half the constant of proportionality.

Yet another view of the small-time problem of Rayleigh analysis follows from an analysis of (131), to determine the nature of its solution. With considerable manipulation, one can show that, when the ε_i are all sufficiently small compared with 1, the difference δa between the solution $\hat{a}$ of (131) and the Rayleigh parameter **a** is given approximately by

$$\delta a = \frac{\sum_{i=1}^{N} \dfrac{z_i'}{z_i}(\overline{\varepsilon} - \varepsilon_i)}{\sum_{j=1}^{N} \dfrac{z_j'}{z_j}\left[\left(\dfrac{z'}{z}\right)_{av} - \dfrac{z_j'}{z_j}\right]} \qquad (134)$$

where

$$\overline{\varepsilon} \equiv \frac{1}{N}\sum_{1}^{N}\varepsilon_i, \quad \left(\frac{z'}{z}\right) \equiv \frac{1}{N}\sum_{1}^{N}\frac{z_i'}{z_i} \qquad (135)$$

and where z_i and z_i' denote $z_i(\hat{a})$ and $z_i'(\hat{a})$, respectively.

One can also show—again with a good deal of manipulation—that when $\sqrt{a}t_i \leq \gamma \ll 1$ for all **i**, then the denominator of (134) is of order γ^8, while the numerator is of order γ^4. Thus, for small values of γ, the solution (134) amplifies the observation errors of the $\tilde{y}_i$ strongly. More explicitly, (134) shows that δa is a linear combination of independent, zero-mean normal random variables with standard deviation σ. Thus, δa is a zero-mean normal random variable. The fact that the numerator of (134) is of order γ^4 while its denominator is of order γ^8 for small γ means that the standard deviation of δa will be a larger and larger multiple of σ as γ grows smaller and smaller.

Experience indicates that inferences from the Rayleigh model are likely to be unsatisfactory unless the observations include data for some times t_i that are at least nearly as large as the time t_p of peak expenditure rate.

This state of affairs does not, however, mean that the Rayleigh model cannot be helpful when only data for small time values are available. While for such cases the Rayleigh model by itself is not useful, often the analyst has more information than just a few initial values of the development program's costs. She may, for example, know from sources independent of the data that a certain value of completion time is likely, or she may know a distribution of completion times. Such additional information can be used with the Rayleigh model to make helpful estimates.

One does so by using the small-time limit of the $dz_i(a)$ shown in (132), to infer only the product **ad**, rather than both **a** and **d**. Given an estimate for $q \equiv ad$ and an independent estimate for **a**, one can produce an estimate for **d**. To estimate **q**, in the context of the multiplicative error we have assumed, one solves

$$\min_q \sum_1^N \left[\frac{\tilde{y}_i}{q(t_i^2 - t_{i-1}^2)} - 1 \right]^2 \qquad \textbf{(136)}$$

For example, carrying out this procedure with the first five points of Table 5 leads to an estimate of 7.597×10^{-4} for the product **ad**. If we have an independent estimate of, say, 2,000 days for completion time, and infer **a** from (122), we would estimate **a** as 8.766×10^{-7}. Combining these two estimates of **ad** and **a** gives an estimate for **d** of 867 constant-dollar units. If we take the conventional final cost t_f as 97 percent of **d**, then our estimate for final cost is 841 constant-dollar units. This is certainly very much better than what resulted from the attempt to use the five data points and the Rayleigh model alone.

ERROR STATISTICS

In general the estimates of **a** and **d**, like the estimates of t_f and **d**, are correlated random variables. Thus, it is helpful to consider the statistics of their errors jointly, as we will do in this section.

A full analysis of the nonlinear estimator for **a** and **d** provided, respectively, by the solution of (131) and (130) is beyond the scope of this book. A linearized analysis is often applicable, however, and it is fairly tractable. In making it, we assume that the ε_i and the differences between the estimators and the quantities estimated are all first order in some parameter **s**, and **s** << 1. We neglect terms of second order in **s**.

Equation (134), derived under that linearization, has the form

$$\delta a = \sum_{1}^{N} A_i \varepsilon_i \equiv A \cdot \varepsilon \tag{137}$$

After some manipulation, one can show that, in the linearized approximation,

$$\delta d \equiv \hat{d} - d = D \cdot \varepsilon \tag{138}$$

where

$$D_i = \hat{d}\left[\frac{1}{N} - \left(\frac{z'}{z}\right)_{ave} A_i\right] \qquad (139)$$

Also, still in the linearized analysis,

$$\delta t_f = T \cdot \varepsilon; \quad T = -0.14258\hat{t}_f^3 A \qquad (140)$$

Since *completion time* and *limiting cost* are perhaps the most interesting results of the Rayleigh forecast, we will carry out the linearized error analysis for these variables. It follows immediately from the representations (138) and (140) that δt_f and δd are zero-mean, bivariate normal random variables.[36] The standard deviations of these variables, and their correlation ρ, are given by

$$\sigma_{tf} = \sigma\sqrt{T \cdot T}; \quad \sigma_d = \sigma\sqrt{D \cdot D}; \quad \rho = \frac{T \cdot D}{\sqrt{(D \cdot D)(T \cdot T)}} \qquad (141)$$

With these parameters, which determine the bivariate normal distribution of δt_f and δd, one can extract any information desired about the errors of a Rayleigh estimate, given an estimate for σ. For that estimate, we take

$$\sigma \approx \sqrt{\frac{1}{N}\sum_1^N\left(\frac{\tilde{y}_i}{\hat{d}z_i(\hat{a})} - 1\right)^2} \qquad (142)$$

As an example, let's explore the error statistics for the 10-point estimate of the example program made above.

---

[36]This multivariate distribution is discussed in many references. A widely available one is the "Abramowitz and Stegun Handbook," specifically, Abramowitz, A., and I. A. Stegun, *Handbook of Mathematical Functions*. First published by the United States Government Printing Office in 1965, the work has had many editions. In the tenth GPO edition (which is reproduced in the eighth printing of the Dover Press edition), the material on the bivariate normal distribution begins on page 936.

Evaluating **D**, **T**, and the estimate for σ is a straightforward task. For the bivariate normal distribution of δt_f and δd, contours of constant probability are curves on which

$$\frac{\delta t_f^2}{\sigma_{t_f}^2} - 2\rho \frac{\delta t_f \delta d}{\sigma_{t_f} \sigma_d} + \frac{\delta d^2}{\sigma_d} = \text{const} \tag{143}$$

Some contours of constant probability for t_f and **d** are shown in Figure 31. In Figure 31, the point corresponding to the estimated values of t_f and **d** is shown with a ★. For this case, δt_f and δd are strongly correlated: their correlation ρ is 90 percent. The high correlation also is evidenced by the concentration of the contours along a line for which δt_f is proportional to δd.

It is straightforward work to calculate curves corresponding to given confidence in t_f and **d,** using properties of the bivariate normal distribution. For example, the curve with square point-markers in Figure 31 is a 75 percent confidence curve: in the linearized analysis, the probability is 75 percent that the actual t_f and **d** are inside this curve.

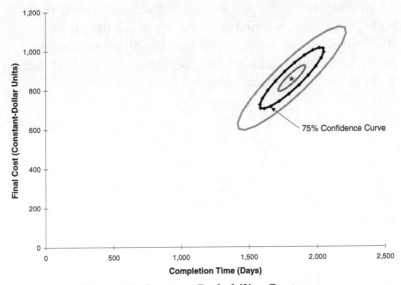

Figure 31. Constant Probability Contours

DISTRIBUTIONS OTHER THAN RAYLEIGH

The justification for using the Rayleigh distribution is empirical. Since development environments may change, it is natural to ask if other distributions than the Rayleigh might sometimes be more appropriate. Gallagher and Lee[37] give a generalized model that covers Rayleigh distributions as well as the distribution developed by Paar[38]. This model is

$$\frac{dv}{dt} = F(v) \tag{144}$$

---

[37] Gallagher, M. A., and D. A. Lee, "Final-Cost Estimates for Research & Development Programs Conditioned on Realized Costs," *Military Operations Research*, Volume 2, 1996, pp. 51-68.

[38] Paar, F. N., loc. cit. Ante.

In (144), **v(t)** is the project's earned value at time **t**, and **F(v)** is a function describing the rate at which the project absorbs resources. Different **F(v)** lead to different resource profiles. A simple calculus exercise shows that the **F(v)** that leads to the Rayleigh distribution is

$$F(v) = ad\sqrt{-\frac{1}{a}\ln\left(1-\frac{v}{d}\right)}\left(1-\frac{v}{d}\right) \tag{145}$$

Determining what function **F(v)** is appropriate is a task for the kind of nonparametric system identification methods mentioned in Chapter 1. The same data that give empirical justification for the Rayleigh distribution also support the **F(v)** of (147), of course.

SUMMARY

In this chapter we saw how to use the empirically justified Norden-Rayleigh model of the expenditure patterns of development programs to find period-by-period spreads of an estimate of the total cost of a development program. We saw how to use the model to estimate cost-to-go of a development program, given costs in some set of initial time periods, and we observed some limitations on this, imposed by mathematical features of the Norden-Rayleigh model.

In the following chapter, we turn from estimating costs of development programs to a topic in estimating operating and maintenance costs.

ENGINEERING AND STATISTICAL CONSIDERATIONS FOR ESTIMATING CERTAIN OPERATING AND SUPPORT COSTS

In recent work, Wallace[39,40] points out that simplistic models that estimate the resource consumption of military aircraft as proportional to flying hours are wrong. In Footnote 39, Wallace cites many sources identifying other factors that should be considered. He uses data for C-5A, C-5B, and F-15C aircraft operations, to develop improved models that include some of those factors.

In this chapter, for a concluding example of the benefits of rational mathematical modeling and statistics in cost estimating, I'll develop a quantitative model of removal rates for aircraft from first principles. The model includes the five factors deemed most important in Footnote 39, and it takes a simple form that can be calibrated and tested readily, given appropriate data. The model may be adjusted readily to

---

[39]Wallace, John M., *Mission Effects on Aircraft Reliability: Another Look at an Old Idea*, Report IR311RD1, Logistics Management Institute, June 1993.

[40]Wallace, John M., "O&S Best Practices," Plenary Session Presentation, 30th Annual Department of Defense Cost Analysis Symposium, Williamsburg, Virginia, February 13, 1996.

account for variations in certain factors, for example, for temporary changes in basing.

MATHEMATICAL PRELIMINARIES

We begin by collecting a few classical results from reliability modeling. A basic one is the Poisson process.

THE POISSON PROCESS

A useful model that characterizes many failure processes starts with three ideas (assumptions):

- The probability of failure happening in a time interval $\left(t - \frac{\Delta t}{2}, t + \frac{\Delta t}{2}\right)$ is proportional to Δt, and is independent of **t**.

- Failures in disjoint time intervals are statistically independent events.

- The probability of more than one failure in a sufficiently small time interval is negligibly small.

Let $P_0(t)$ denote the probability that no failure has occurred in time **t** after the time at which a failure last occurred. Let's see how $P_0(t)$ evolves with time. By the second assumption, $P_0(t + \Delta t)$ will be equal to the probability that there has been no failure in time **t**, times the probability that there is no failure in the interval $(t, t + \Delta t)$. By the first and third assumptions, that latter probability is equal to $1 - \lambda \Delta t$, where λ is a constant, if we take Δt sufficiently small. Thus, except for negligible terms,

$$P_0(t + \Delta t) = P_0(t)(1 - \lambda \Delta t) \qquad (146)$$

for Δt sufficiently small. Equation (146) implies

$$\frac{P_0(t + \Delta t) - P(t)}{\Delta t} = -\lambda P_0(t) \tag{147}$$

taking the limit of both sides of (147) as Δt tends to zero[41] gives

$$P_0'\ (t) = -\lambda P_0(t) \tag{148}$$

since no failure should occur over zero time,

$$P_0(0) = 1 \tag{149}$$

The solution of (148) and (149) is

$$P_0(t) = e^{-\lambda t} \tag{150}$$

The probability that the next failure occurs in the interval $(t, t + \Delta t)$ following its predecessor is the probability that no failure occurs on $(0, t)$ times the probability that a failure does occur in $(t, t + \Delta t)$. By virtue of the first and third assumptions (bulleted on the previous page) and Equation (150), this is

$$P_0(t)(\lambda \Delta t) = \lambda e^{-\lambda t} \Delta t \tag{151}$$

It follows that the time between failures has the probability distribution function

$$p(t) = \lambda e^{-\lambda t} \tag{152}$$

The distribution function of (152) is known as the exponential distribution. We can evaluate the mean time between failures (MTBF) as

---

[41]The mathematically alert will have noticed that our derivation justifies only taking the limit as Δt tends to zero from above. If we add the assumption that $P_0(t)$ is differentiable, we get to (148).

$$< t >= \int_0^\infty t \lambda e^{-\lambda t} dt = \frac{1}{\lambda} \tag{153}$$

Also, we can determine the probability that precisely **N** failures will occur on **(0,t)** as a function of **t**. The probability that precisely **N** failures have occurred on $(0, t + \Delta t)$ is the probability that **N** failures have occurred on **(0, t)** and no failure occurs on $(t, t + \Delta t)$, *or*, **N** − 1 failures have occurred on **(0, t)** and a failure occurs on $(t, t + \Delta t)$. Let $P_N(t)$ be the probability that **N** failures occur on a time interval **(0, t)**. Then, by an extension of the arguments that led to (150),

$$P_N(t + \Delta t) = P_N(t)(1 - \lambda \Delta t) + P_{N-1}(t) \lambda \Delta t \tag{154}$$

Equation (154) leads to

$$P'_N(t) + \lambda P_N(t) = \lambda P_{N-1}(t) \tag{155}$$

since **N** failures cannot happen on arbitrarily short time,

$$P_N(0) = 0 \tag{156}$$

The initial value problem of (155) subject to (156) can be solved immediately by elementary means. For example, it follows from (155) and (156) that the Laplace transforms $G_N(s)$ of the $P_N(t)$ satisfy the recursion relation

$$G_N(s) = \frac{\lambda}{s + \lambda} G_{N-1}(s) \tag{157}$$

Equation (157) implies

$$G_N(s) = \left(\frac{\lambda}{s + \lambda} \right)^N G_0(s) \tag{158}$$

and, since by (150)

$$G_0(s) = \frac{1}{s + \lambda} \tag{159}$$

we have

$$G_N(s) = \frac{\lambda^N}{(s+\lambda)^{N+1}}, N \geq 0 \qquad (160)$$

from which follows by inverting the Laplace transforms,

$$P_N(t) = \frac{(\lambda t)^N}{N!} e^{-\lambda t} \qquad (161)$$

The $P_N(t)$ may be called the Poisson distribution with parameter λt. By summing the series involved, it is not hard to show that the mean and the variance of the Poisson distribution are both equal to λt.

THE BINOMIAL DISTRIBUTION

Another important distribution for reliability studies is the one that gives the distribution of the number of failures observed in N independent trials of an experiment that has only the two outcomes, failure or no failure, and for which the probability of failure is the same for all trials. The probability of a sequence of m failures in N trials is $p^m(1-p)^{N-m}$. To get the probability of observing m failures in N trials, we must multiply that sequence probability by the number of such sequences, i.e., by the number of distinct sequences of m failures and $N-m$ successes.

This is the same counting problem that is solved by the binomial theorem, where the things being counted are sequences in which m factors of the term a appear in N-member sequences of the factors a and b in the expansion of $(a+b)^N$. The count is given by the binomial coefficient $\binom{N}{m}$,

$$\binom{N}{m} \equiv \frac{N!}{(N-m)!m!} \qquad \textbf{(162)}$$

Thus, the probability of observing **m** failures in **N** independent trials of an experiment for which failure and no failure are the only possible outcomes, for each of which the probability of failure is **p**, is

$$B(m, N, p) = \binom{N}{m} p^{m}(1-p)^{N-m} \qquad \textbf{(163)}$$

It is not difficult to show that the mean and variance of the binomial distribution are **Np** and **Np(1–p)**, respectively.

NORMAL APPROXIMATIONS TO THE POISSON AND BINOMIAL DISTRIBUTIONS

It is quite useful in our model development that both the binomial and the discrete Poisson distributions are closely approximated by normal distributions, in certain cases. The cases that interest us are the binomial distribution when the number of trials **N** is large, and the discrete Poisson distribution when the parameter λt is large. Actually, the two "large" parameters do not have to be all that big for the normal approximation to be a good one. Figure 32 shows the binomial distribution for **N**=100 trials and **p** = 0.12, and the normal distribution with the same mean and variance.

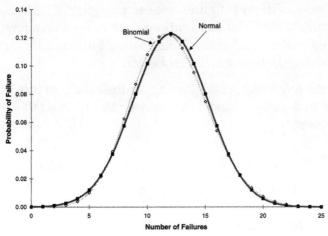

Figure 32. Binomial Distribution and Approximating Normal Distribution

Figure 33 shows a discrete Poisson distribution for $\lambda t = 100$, together with the normal distribution that has the same mean and variance.

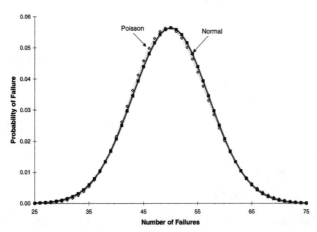

Figure 33. Discrete Poisson Distribution and Approximating Normal Distribution

In view of the two figures, we can confidently approximate binomial distributions with more than a few hundred trials, and discrete Poisson distributions with means larger than 100, by normal distributions.

In the following section, we apply the results of this section to develop a model of removal rates for aircraft operations.

A MODEL OF REMOVAL RATES FOR AIRCRAFT OPERATIONS

The five principal factors cited by Wallace[39, p. 113] as likely to affect the rate at which failures cause parts to be removed from aircraft are: the operations tempo (OPTEMPO), which is the mean number of flying hours that the aircraft in the fleet experience per period; the sortie rate; the sortie length; the number of cycles (i.e., takeoffs and landings) per sortie; and the ground environment in which the fleet is kept when not flying. We can develop a model addressing each of these factors, as follows.

Let the probability that a takeoff induces a removal-requiring failure be P_T, and let the probability that a landing does that be P_L. Then the probability that a takeoff-landing cycle induces such a failure is

$$P_C = 1 - (1 - P_T)(1 - P_L) \qquad (164)$$

Accordingly, the probability that m_c such failures will be induced by N takeoff-landing cycles is given by the binomial distribution $B(m_c, N, P_C)$.

Please note: From this point on, we will refer to "failure requiring a removal" simply as "failure." This considerably simplifies the text.

Now, let the process by which flying induces failures be a Poisson process with parameter λ_F, and let the process by which the ground environment induces failures be a Poisson process with parameter λ_G. Then the number of failures induced by flying t_F hours is a discrete Poisson distribution with parameter $\lambda_F t_F$, and the number of failures induced by existing in the ground environment t_G hours has a discrete Poisson distribution with parameter $\lambda_G t_G$.

Now, let us assume that the number N of cycles, and the mean number of failures produced by both flight and ground operations, are all larger than 100. In this case, the normal approximations to the binomial distribution of cycle-induced failures, and to the two discrete Poisson distributions of flight- and ground-induced failures, will all be approximated well by normal distributions. Under this assumption, the cycle-induced failures will have the normal distribution with mean NP_C and variance $NP_C(1 - P_C)$. The flight-induced failures will be normally distributed with mean and variance both equal to $\lambda_F t_F$, while the failures induced by the ground environment will have the normal distribution with mean and variance both given by $\lambda_G t_G$.

The total number of failures induced by N cycles, t_F flight hours, and t_G hours in the ground environment will be the sum of three normal random variables. Such a sum is again normally distributed. Its mean is equal to the sum of the means, and its variance is equal to the sum of the variances, of the three summed variables. Thus, the total number of failures will have mean $NP_C + \lambda_F t_F + \lambda_G t_G$, and variance $NP_C(1 - P_C) + \lambda_F t_F + \lambda_G t_G$. This is the model for removals that we have developed from first principles.

If we assume that aircraft in possession of an operational unit are either flying or in the ground environment, then

$$t_G = t_P - t_F \qquad (165)$$

where t_P denotes the number of hours that aircraft are in the unit's possession. In this case, the mean and variance of the distribution of failures are, respectively,

$NP_C + (\lambda_F - \lambda_G)t_F + \lambda_G t_P$ and $NP_C(1 - P_C) + |\lambda_F - \lambda_G|t_F + \lambda_G t_P$.

These expressions show an interesting feature of our model: flight time per period may either increase *or decrease* both the mean and the variance of the number of replacements, depending on whether or not $\lambda_F > \lambda_G$. There is evidence that increasing flight hours per period can indeed decrease replacement rates.[42]

Relating model parameters to the five parameters of interest is straightforward: T_G addresses the ground environment directly; FH = OPTEMPO × TAI, where TAI is total aircraft inventory; $N = r_s \times c_s$, where r_s is the sortie rate and c_s is the number of cycles per sortie, and so on.

CALIBRATING THE MODEL

We have developed a model for the distribution of the number of removals generated by N landing-takeoff cycles, t_F flying hours, and t_P hours in the unit's possession. Fortunately, data on just those factors are accumulated by some military departments. How shall we use them to calibrate the model?

We must give the matter some thought, because our model is intrinsically heteroscedastic. If the parameters by which we intend to express variations in removals do in fact vary from

---

[42]Goodson, Wilfred L., "Readiness and Sustainability: How's Your Estimate?," *Budgeting for Sustainability*, John C. Honig, Editor, Operations Research Society of America, May 1986 (as cited in Footnote 39).

period to period, then so does the variance of the number of removals, according to our model.

We can in fact generate maximum-likelihood estimators of λ_F, λ_G, and P_c. That is, we can choose these parameters to maximize the likelihood of an observed sequence of replacements. Because the variances differ from period to period, this maximization does not reduce to a simple method like linear regression. It can, however, be done numerically.

Calibrated in this way, the model offers the possibility of adjustments to represent the effects of changes in operations. For example, if a unit's aircraft are stationed away from their usual base for some periods and the ground environment at the new station is thought to be more or less likely to induce failures than that of the usual base, then a different λ_G, λ_G', say, can be assigned to those periods. The likelihood of the observed sequence of replacements is then maximized over $\lambda_F, \lambda_G, \lambda_G'$, and P_c. Then, when aircraft are stationed at their usual base, one may estimate the distribution of removals as the one corresponding to λ_F, λ_G, and P_c. If again the unit were stationed at the other base, one would estimate the distribution of removals as that corresponding to λ_F, λ_G', and P_c.

AN EXAMPLE

Table 6 shows the flying hours, hour in possession, sorties, landings, and removals for C-5B operations during 16 monthly periods:

Month	Date	Flying Hours	Hours in Possession	Sorties	Landings	Removals
1	Apr 89	3,248	31,006	821	3,121	1,707
2	May 89	3,381	34,742	931	3,150	2,175
3	Jun 89	3,024	35,648	839	2,860	1,938
4	Jul 89	2,953	37,200	769	2,571	1,765
5	Aug 89	3,110	37,188	888	2,747	1,890
6	Sep 89	3,650	35,943	1,058	2,974	1,628
7	Oct 89	3,205	37,200	900	2,878	1,834
8	Nov 89	3,125	35,919	866	2,739	1,894
9	Dec 89	3,327	37,200	876	2,065	1,758
10	Jan 90	2,994	37,115	816	2,796	2,173
11	Feb 90	3,088	33,600	818	2,762	1,423
12	Mar 90	3,205	37,200	906	2,891	1,848
13	Apr 90	2,975	35,976	842	2,626	1,960
14	May 90	2,892	36,790	791	2,890	1,977
15	Jun 90	2,725	34,560	773	2,965	1,573
16	Jul 90	2,545	37,200	724	2,739	1,857

Table 6. Data for C-5B Aircraft Operations

Figure 34 shows the result of calibrating our model on these data, assuming that the parameters λ_F, λ_G, and P_c are the same for all periods.

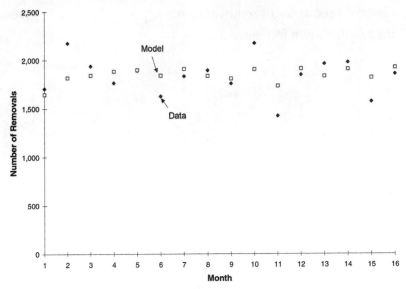

Figure 34. Initial Calibration of the Model, Assuming Constant Parameters

While the model captures some of the observed variation, clearly months 2, 6, 10, 11, and 15 are not treated well. In developing a really usable estimating relation, a task far beyond the scope of this book, one would determine what (if anything!) about the C-5B fleet's operations were different for these periods, and recalibrate accordingly.

Purely as an illustrative example, let us assume that the reason for the outlying points was differing ground environments. Since the model is sharply too low for months 2 and 10, and sharply too high for months 6, 11, and 15, let us introduce two new λ_G parameters, one for periods 2 and 10, and another for periods 6, 11, and 15.

Then, we recalibrate the model, with ground environment parameters λ_{G_1} in periods 2 and 10; λ_{G_2} in periods 6, 11 and 15; and λ_G in all other periods. Maximizing the likelihood of the observed sequence of removals over $\lambda_{G1}, \lambda_{G2}, \lambda_G$, and P_c gives the result shown in Figure 35.

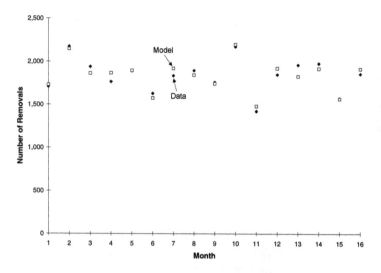

**Figure 35. Recalibration Result, Adjusting Two
Ground-Environment Parameters**

Naturally, the calibration of Figure 35 is a considerable improvement. If the introduction of the two different ground-environment parameters were justified by data, one might consider basing estimates of removals on the result.

SUMMARY

In this chapter, we saw how rational mathematical modeling and statistics can be used to make a model of the rates of equipment removal for aircraft fleets. The model includes effects of fleet operational factors widely held to affect replacement rates. At least on first inspection, it appears to offer a potentially useful alternative to models that characterize replacement rate as a function of flying hours alone.

APPENDIX

A VISUAL BASIC FUNCTION FOR A(L, U, b)

Here is a listing of the Visual Basic code to calculate Asher's approximation, as discussed in Chapter 3. To evaluate **A(L, U, b)** in Microsoft Excel® spreadsheets, copy the following lines into a module. In the spreadsheet, or in other Visual Basic code, simply evaluate **A(L, U, b)** as

```
= za(L, U, b)
```

where **L**, **U**, and **b** are quantities identified in specific worksheet cells.

The function for **za(L, U, b)** is defined below. It in turn calls two other functions, **zs(L, U, b)** and **zze(L, U, b)**, also defined below.

```
'***************************************************
Function za(L, U As Long, b As Double) As Double
    If (L >= 4) Then
        za = zze(L, U, b)
    ElseIf (U <= 4) Then
        za = zs(L, U, b)
    Else
        za = zs(L, 4, b) + zze(5, U, b)
    End If
End Function
```

```
'* * * * * * * * * * * * * * * * * * * * * * * * * * * * * * * * * * * * * * * * * *

Function zze(L, U As Long, b As Double) As Double
    Dim bb(1 To 10) As Double
    Dim c, s, t, uu, ll, tu, tl, h, r, kk, p, q,_
        uc, lc, u2, 12 As Double
    Dim i As Integer

    bb(1) = 0.16666667:      bb(2) = -0.033333333
    bb(3) = 0.023809523:     bb(4) = -0.0333333333
    bb(5) = 0.075757576:     bb(6) = -0.25311355
    bb(7) = 1.16666667:      bb(8) = -7.0921569
    bb(9) = 54.971178:       bb(10) = -529.12424


    c = 1 + b
    uu = U + 0.5
    ll = L - 0.5
    uc = uu ^ c
    lc = ll ^ c
    p = uc/c: q = lc/c
    s = p - q


    u2 = uu ^ (-2): 12 = ll ^ (-2)
    h = 2: r = 1: i = 0: kk = b + 2: ll = b + 3
    tl = 1


    Do
        h = 0.25 * h: i = i + 1
        r = 2 * i * (2 * i - 1) * r
        kk = kk - 2: ll = ll - 2
        p = kk * ll * p * u2
```

```
        q = kk * l1 * q * l2
        t = (1 - h) * bb(i) * (p - q)/r
        t1 = Abs(t/s)
        s = s - t
    Loop While ((t1 > 0.00000001) And (i <= 9))
    zze = s
End Function


'**************************************************
Function zs(L, U As Long, b As Double) As Double
    Dim i As Integer
    Dim s As Double

    s = 0
    For i = L To U
        s = s + i ^ b
    Next i
    zs = s
End Function
```

BIBLIOGRAPHY

Abernethy, T., "An Application of the Rayleigh Distribution to Contract Cost Data," Master's Thesis, U.S. Navy Naval Postgraduate School, 1984, directed by Professor Dan C. Boger.

Abramowitz, M., and I. A. Stegun, *Handbook of Mathematical Functions*, United States Government Printing Office, 1965.

Asher, H., *Cost-Quantity Relationships in the Airframe Industry*, RAND, Santa Monica, 1956.

Cheney, W., *Introduction to Approximation Theory*, Second Edition, Chelsea, New York, 1991.

De Soer, C., and M. Vidyasagar, *Feedback Systems: Input-Output Properties*, Academic Press, New York, 1975.

Dutton, J. M., A. Thomas, and J. Butler, "The History of Cost Progress Functions as a Managerial Technology," *Business History Review*, Volume 58, 1984.

Gallagher, M. A., and D. A. Lee, "Final-Cost Estimates for Research & Development Programs Conditioned on Realized Costs," *Military Operations Research*, Volume 2, 1996.

Goodson, Wilfred L., "Readiness and Sustainability: How's Your Estimate?," *Budgeting for Sustainability*, John C. Honig, Editor, Operations Research Society of America, May 1986.

Gran, S., "A Course in Ocean Engineering," *Developments in Marine Technology*, Number 8, Elsevier Science Publishers, Netherlands, 1992.

Hahne, H. V., *Handbook of Engineering Mechanics*, W. Flugge, Editor, McGraw-Hill, New York, 1962.

Hemm, R., *A Down-to-Earth Approach to Space Launch*, Logistics Management Institute internal paper, 1996.

Hildebrand, F. B., *Introduction to Numerical Analysis*, Second Edition, McGraw-Hill, New York, 1974.

Hoel, P. G., *Introduction to Mathematical Statistics*, Fifth Edition, Wiley, New York, 1984.

Judge, George G., et al, *The Theory and Practice of Econometrics*, Wiley, New York, 1980.

Lee, D. A., and D. Audley, "Ill Posed and Well Posed Problems in System Identification," *IEEE Transactions on Automatic Control*, AC-19, 1974.

Lee, D. A., M. A. Gallagher, and M. R. Hogue, "Determining a Budget Profile from a R&D Cost Estimate," to appear in the *Journal of Cost Analysis*.

Lee, D. A., M. R. Hogue, and D. C. Hoffman, "Time Histories of Expenditures for Defense Acquisition Programs in the Development Phase—Norden-Rayleigh and Other Models," presented at the 1993 Annual Meeting of the International Society of Parametric Analysis.

Marden, Luis, "Restoring Old Ironsides," *National Geographic*, Volume 191, June 1997.

Maybeck, P. S., *Stochastic Models, Estimation, and Control*, Volume 2, Academic Press, New York, 1982.

Moses, O. D., "Extensions to the Cost-Progress Model: An Analysis of Factors Influencing Unit Cost of Weapon Systems," to appear in the *Journal of Cost Analysis*.

Norden, V. P., "Useful Tools for Project Management," *Management of Production*, M. K. Stan, Editor, Penguin, Baltimore, 1970.

Paar, F. N., "An Alternative to the Rayleigh Curve Model for Software Development," *IEEE Transactions on Software Engineering*, May 1980.

Rogerson, W., *Regulatory Lag, Incentives for Process Innovation, and the Defense Procurement Process*, Lecture Notes, Department of Economics, Northwestern University, November 1992.

Sage, A. P., and J. L. Melsa, *System Identification*, Academic Press, New York, 1971.

Slotine, J. J., and W. Li, *Applied Non-Linear Control*, Prentice-Hall, New York, 1991.

Wallace, John M., *Mission Effects on Aircraft Reliability: Another Look at an Old Idea*, Report IR311RD1, Logistics Management Institute, June 1993.

Wallace, John M., "O&S Best Practices," Plenary Session Presentation, 30th Annual Department of Defense Cost Analysis Symposium, Williamsburg, Virginia, February 13, 1996.

Watkins, H., "An Application of Rayleigh Curve Theory to Contract Cost Estimation and Control," Master's Thesis, U.S. Navy Naval Postgraduate School, 1982, directed by Professor Dan C. Boger.

Watson, Donald S., *Price Theory and Its Uses*, Third Edition, Houghton-Mifflin, Boston, 1972.

Witt, Sandra L., et al, *Electro-Optical, Missile, Radar and Avionics System Cost Research*: Volume 1, *Radar Production Cost Model*, and Volume 3, *Missile Production Cost Model*, Management Consulting and Research, Incorporated, Report TR-8740-2, May 1988.

Wright, T. P., "Factors Affecting the Cost of Airplanes," *Journal of Aerospace Science*, Volume 3, 1936.

Yelle, L. E., "The Learning Curve: Historical Review and Comprehensive Survey," *Decision Sciences*, Volume 10, 1979.

ABOUT THE AUTHOR

Educated at the University of Missouri (BSEE 1959), Brown University (Sc. M. 1961), and the Illinois Institute of Technology (Ph. D. 1963), David Lee was successively a research mathematician, group leader, and Director of the Applied Mathematics Research Laboratory in the U.S. Air Force's Aerospace Research Laboratories. As Head of the Air Force Institute of Technology's Mathematics Department, he developed statistics and analysis courses for the Institute's master's degree program in cost analysis. From 1985 through 1993, as Director of the Operations Research/Procurement Planning Division in the Office of the Assistant Secretary of Defense, Program Analysis and Evaluation, he was responsible to the Chairman of the OSD Cost Analysis Improvement Group for preparing estimates of the costs of major acquisition programs in the Department of Defense. Since his retirement from federal civilian service, Dr. Lee has been a busier consultant than his wife wishes him to be.

Recognition of Dr. Lee's work includes the Tau Beta Pi Outstanding Instructor Award, the Faculty-Alumni Award of the University of Missouri-Columbia, the Barchi prize of the Military Operations Research Society, the Presidential Rank of SES Meritorious Executive, and the Department of Defense Award for Distinguished Civilian Service.

INDEX

R

random variables
 bivariate normal, 109
rate slope, 14
Rayleigh, 93
 completion time, 109
 forecasting, 98
 limiting cost, 109
 small-time problem, 103
removal rates, 113
resource consumption, 113
Riemann zeta function, 37
Rogerson, 29

S

segment exponent, 22
square law, 80
system identification, 4

U

unit model, 10
 expanded, 14

V

Visual Basic, 127
Volterra integral, 6

W

Wallace, 113
Wright model, 11
 lot costs, 34

Y

Young's modulus, 86

NOTES

NOTES

NOTES

NOTES

NOTES

NOTES

DH

658.
155
2
LEE